REVISE FO

NEAB

COORDINATED

science

NIGEL ENGLISH

HIGHER

Heinemann Educational Publishers
Halley Court, Jordan Hill, Oxford, OX2 8EJ
a division of Reed Educational & Professional Publishing Ltd

Heinemann is a registered trademark of Reed Educational & Professional Publishing Ltd.

OXFORD   FLORENCE   PRAGUE   MADRID   ATHENS
MELBOURNE   AUCKLAND   KUALA LUMPUR   SINGAPORE
TOKYO   IBADAN   NAIROBI   KAMPALA   JOHANNESBURG
GABORONE   PORTSMOUTH NH (USA)   CHICAGO
MEXICO CITY   SAO PAULO

© Nigel English, 1997

First published 1997

ISBN 0 435 10165 X

01 00 99 98 97
10 9 8 7 6 5 4 3 2 1

Edited by Sarah Ware and Andrew Nash

Designed and typeset by Ken Vail Graphic Design

Illustrated by Nick Hawken, Graeme Morris (Ken Vail Graphic Design) and John Plumb

Cover design by Threefold Design

Cover artwork by Stephen May

Printed and bound in the UK by Bath Press

Acknowledgements
The author and publishers would like to thank the following for permission to use photographs:

page 1: Tony Stone, *page 41:* Sygma, *page 85:* Tony Stone.

The author and publishers would like to thank the Northern Examinations and Assessment Board for permission to reproduce exam questions.

The publishers have made every effort to trace the copyright holders, but if they have inadvertently overlooked any, they will be pleased to make the necessary arrangements at the first opportunity.

Picture research by Natalie Stewart

From the author
I would particularly like to thank my family, Chris, Philip and Katharine, for their help and forbearance in writing this book.

Contents

How to use this book

This revision guide contains all the material in the NEAB Coordinated Science scheme. It covers the Higher Tier of the syllabus.

As you approach the exam in your course:

Work through sections of the book. Pace yourself – do one double page spread at a time and look at the notes you have made in class on this topic.

Try the questions at the end of every double page spread to check that you really understand the topic.

Check your answers under *Answers to end of spread questions*. Go back over anything you find difficult.

Do the exam style questions at the end of each Section. These are in the same style as the ones you will have to do in the real exam so they are very good practice.

Check your answers against the *Answers to exam questions*. Take care to cover all the points needed to get full marks. Go back over areas you find difficult.

The words in **bold** are all key words you need to know. A useful revision idea would be to build up your own glossary of these as you work through the book. For quick reference to a word or topic use the *Index* at the back of the book.

Don't forget, you only need to revise AT2 for the biology exam, AT3 for the chemistry exam and AT4 for the physics exam. The three exams are usually held on three separate days.

AT2

Life Processes and Living Things

Cells

Cells make up animals and plants. Most animal cells have:

- a nucleus that controls what the cell does
- cytoplasm in which the chemical reactions take place
- a cell membrane which controls the passage of substances in and out of the cell.

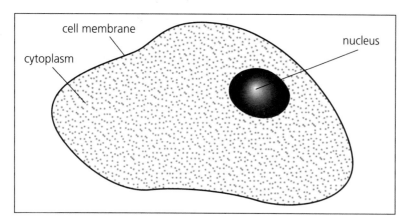

A typical animal cell

Specialised cells may group together to do a job (e.g. muscles and glands). These are called **tissues**.

Organs (e.g. the heart and liver) are made up from tissues. Organs combine to form **systems** (e.g. the circulatory system and the nervous system).

Eating and digestion

The human digestive system (often called the gut) includes the gullet, stomach, liver, pancreas, small intestine and large intestine. Its job is to turn food we eat into a form which can be used by the body cells. Its tissues include **muscles** to move food along and **glands** to make the enzymes which digest the food.

Much of the food we eat is insoluble (e.g. starches, proteins and fats). This food needs to be digested in the gut so that the large insoluble lumps are broken down into small soluble molecules which can be absorbed into and carried by the blood. This breakdown of larger molecules into smaller ones is speeded up (catalysed) by **enzymes**.

Enzymes break down starch (carbohydrates) to sugars; proteins to amino acids; and fats (lipids) to fatty acids and glycerol. The enzymes are produced at different points in the digestive system.

The soluble molecules are absorbed into the blood through the wall of the small intestine. Some food cannot be digested and this passes into the large intestine. Here, most of the water is absorbed from it. The remainder passes out of the body as faeces. Most of the faeces is indigestible food and it leaves the body by the anus.

 Help

The names of the enzymes are related to the food that they work on, so:

- carbohydrases break down carbohydrates
- proteases break down proteins
- lipases break down lipids (fats).

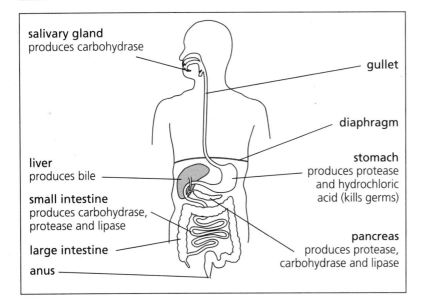

salivary gland
produces carbohydrase

gullet

diaphragm

stomach
produces protease
and hydrochloric
acid (kills germs)

liver
produces bile

small intestine
produces carbohydrase,
protease and lipase

large intestine

anus

pancreas
produces protease,
carbohydrase and lipase

The human digestive system

Bile is produced in the liver and stored in the gall bladder. It has two functions.

- As food enters the small intestine bile neutralises the acid added to it in the stomach. It makes conditions in the small intestine alkaline, allowing the enzymes to work there more effectively.

- It breaks down large fat globules into smaller ones, resulting in a larger surface area for enzymes to work on. This is known as **emulsification**.

Diffusion

The soluble molecules in the small intestine pass into our bloodstream by **diffusion**. This is the movement of particles from a more concentrated solution to one of lower concentration. The blood circulating around the small intestine while a meal is being digested has a lower concentration of simple sugars, amino acids, mineral ions and water than the mixture flowing through the small intestine. The molecules therefore diffuse out through the walls of the small intestine.

This diffusion is helped by the structure of the small intestine walls. They are covered by millions of small, finger-like projections called **villi**. These help the food diffuse through the wall because they:

- slow down the passage of food through the small intestine
- provide a very large surface area for the absorption to take place.

Help

Why is a large surface area important?
This speeds up the rate of absorption because molecules can cross the boundary into the bloodstream across a very wide area instead of a small one. Think of it as a crowd running across an open field instead of trying to crush through a gate!

Questions

1   Make a table showing where the different enzymes are made and what they do.

2   The enzymes in the small intestine need alkaline conditions to work in. What conditions do the stomach enzymes need to work in?

3   Explain why emulsifying fat droplets helps the lipase enzymes to work on them.

The circulatory system

This contains **blood** which is made up of red cells, white cells and platelets carried in a fluid called plasma.

Plasma transports:

- carbon dioxide from all cells in the body's organs to the lungs
- digested food (mostly glucose) from the small intestine to organs
- urea from the liver to the kidneys.

The red cells transport:

- oxygen from the lungs to the cells (organs).

Parts of the blood

Red cells have no nucleus but lots of **haemoglobin**. As the blood passes the lungs the haemoglobin picks up the oxygen to form **oxy-haemoglobin**. The oxygen is released as the blood passes respiring cells.

White cells have a nucleus. They help defend the body against microbes (bacteria).

Platelets are small cell fragments. They don't have a nucleus and help to form clots (scabs over cuts).

Plasma is the liquid part of the blood.

The circulation system

There are two circulation systems:

- one to the lungs
- one to the rest of the body.

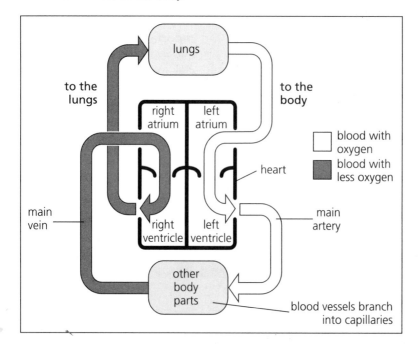

The two circulation systems

The blood enters the two atria of the heart. The muscles of the atria contract and force the blood into the ventricles. The muscles of the ventricles now contract and force the blood out of the heart. This happens on both sides of the heart at the same time.

The different blood vessels

Arteries take blood away from the heart under high pressure. They have thick, muscular, elastic walls so that they don't burst when the heart beats.

Veins bring blood back to the heart under low pressure. They have thinner walls and also have valves along their length to prevent backflow of blood. This is especially important when it is coming back from the feet!

Capillaries are very, very small. Their walls are only one cell thick to allow the exchange of substances with the cells. Oxygen diffuses from the red blood cells in the capillaries to the cells of the body. Carbon dioxide diffuses from these body cells into the blood. Glucose and other useful substances in the plasma diffuse out of the capillary to reach the cells.

Types of blood vessel

Questions

1   What is transported in the plasma?

2   How is the structure of a vein different to that of an artery?

3   What substances are exchanged between the capillaries and the body cells?

4   What are the functions of white cells, red cells and platelets?

5   Trace the journey of a red cell from entering the left atrium of the heart to its arrival at the right atrium.

Breathing and respiration

A 16 year-old has breathed in and out about 75 million times since birth. Why? The answer is to provide oxygen to release energy from food and to get rid of the carbon dioxide produced.

This process is called **aerobic respiration**. All living cells in the body respire. The food which is used in respiration is glucose, a type of sugar and one of the small molecules produced by the digestive system from the complex food that you eat. During aerobic respiration chemical reactions use the glucose and oxygen to release energy. The by-products (waste products) are carbon dioxide and water.

glucose + oxygen → carbon dioxide + water + energy

This energy is used:

- to allow body muscles to contract
- to keep body temperature constant
- to build large useful substances from the small digested ones, for use in the body
- for **active transport** of materials across boundaries.

How do we breathe in?

When we breathe in:

- the muscles between the ribs contract so that the ribs move up and out
- at the same time the muscles of the diaphragm contract and it flattens
- the space inside the thorax (chest) increases and the lungs get larger
- this causes a decrease in air pressure in the lungs
- atmospheric pressure outside is higher, so air rushes in.

... and to breathe out, the process happens in reverse.

Help

Active transport
This is the movement of certain particles from a dilute solution to a more concentrated one. This is opposite to the way substances normally diffuse, so energy is needed to make it happen. It is called *active transport* because substances have to be 'pushed' across cell boundaries against the normal flow.

1 muscles contract making ribcage larger *and* muscles contract pulling down diaphragm making it flatter

3 air rushes in

2 lung volume increases so air pressure decreases

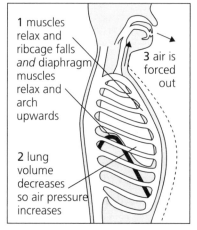

1 muscles relax and ribcage falls *and* diaphragm muscles relax and arch upwards

3 air is forced out

2 lung volume decreases so air pressure increases

Breathing in   *... and breathing out*

How are gases exchanged with the blood?

The oxygen we breathe in diffuses into the air sacs (**alveoli**) of the lungs. It then diffuses through the walls of the alveoli into the surrounding blood capillaries. Carbon dioxide diffuses from the blood in the capillaries into the air sacs.

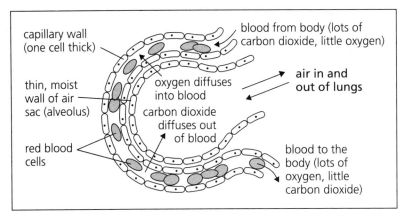

Gas exchange inside the lungs

The lungs have features which make them efficient at exchanging these gases:

• a very large, moist surface area

• a very good capillary blood supply.

Not enough oxygen?

If you run you get tired and your muscles stop contracting efficiently. If there is not enough oxygen for aerobic respiration it slows down and eventually stops.

Anaerobic respiration then takes over. This is respiration without using oxygen. Body cells break down sugar incompletely, into lactic acid, to produce just enough energy for them to work. Lactic acid causes muscle fatigue, so the body can't keep up anaerobic respiration for very long.

When you stop running you still breathe hard. This is because you need the oxygen to break down the lactic acid, releasing carbon dioxide and water. You have built up an **oxygen debt**.

Questions

1   How does the body get the glucose and oxygen needed for respiration?

2   What happens to the carbon dioxide produced by cells during respiration?

3   Explain why the large surface area provided by the alveoli helps the diffusion of gases.

4   Explain why oxygen diffuses into the blood around the lungs and carbon dioxide diffuses out of it.

5   Write a brief description of what happens to the ribs, diaphragm and lungs when you breathe out.

How do humans respond?

The eye

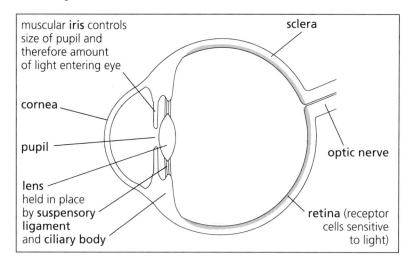

muscular **iris** controls size of pupil and therefore amount of light entering eye

sclera

cornea

pupil

optic nerve

lens held in place by **suspensory ligament** and **ciliary body**

retina (receptor cells sensitive to light)

Cross-section through the human eye

When you look at an object:

- light reflected from the object enters through the cornea
- the cornea and lens focus this light on the retina
- receptor cells in the retina send impulses to the brain along the optic nerve
- the brain interprets the impulses (you 'see' the object) and co-ordinates the necessary response.

The shape of the lens can be changed to focus on near or distant objects, so:

- with near objects the light rays have to be 'bent' more – the lens is quite thick
- with distant objects the light rays need to be 'bent' less – the lens will be much thinner.

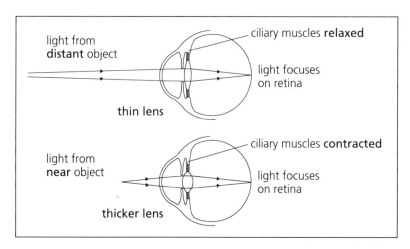

light from **distant** object

ciliary muscles **relaxed**

light focuses on retina

thin lens

light from **near** object

ciliary muscles **contracted**

light focuses on retina

thicker lens

How the eye focuses

The response is automatic. You don't have to think, 'I must change the shape of my lens!' It is a reflex action.

Reflex actions

This is a typical reflex action:

- **Receptors** (e.g. in the retina) send impulses (electrical charges) along a **sensory neurone** (e.g. in the optic nerve) to the central nervous system.
- At the junction with a **relay neurone** a chemical is released. The junction is called a **synapse**.
- This chemical triggers an impulse through the relay neurone.
- At the junction with the correct **motor neurone** a chemical is released again.
- Impulses travel along the motor neurone to the muscle or gland which will do something (the **effector**) in response to the impulse from the neurone.
- The muscle will contract or the gland will produce a hormone or enzyme.

Help

A bundle of neurones make up a nerve.

stimulus
  → **receptor**
      → **co-ordinator** (central nervous system)
          → **effector**
              → **response**

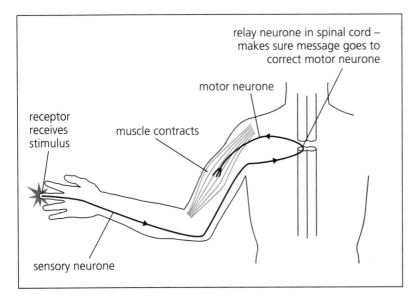

relay neurone in spinal cord –
makes sure message goes to
correct motor neurone

motor neurone

receptor
receives
stimulus

muscle contracts

sensory neurone

A reflex arc

Questions

1   You were watching the television but then looked out of the window at a friend walking through the gate. The television picture and then your friend were both in focus. What happened in your eye to make this happen?

2   You touch a hot kettle. You pull your hand out of the way. Describe the reflex arc which results when this happens.

3   How are impulses carried in the nervous system?

Regulating our internal environment

We produce waste and need to get rid of it. Our waste includes:

- **carbon dioxide** – produced during respiration, excreted through the lungs
- **urea** – produced in the liver by the breakdown of excess amino acids, removed by the kidneys in the urine, which is stored in the bladder.

Other internal conditions which need to be controlled include:

- **water content** of the body – water is lost from the lungs in breathing out and through the skin in sweating; excess water is lost in the urine
- the **ion content** of the body – ions are lost through sweating and in urine
- **temperature** – it is vital to maintain the temperature at which body enzymes work best
- the level of **sugar** in the bloodstream.

Hormones co-ordinate much of what happens inside us. They are carried in the bloodstream and act on specific organs.

The kidneys

Blood arriving at the kidneys contains many useful substances (e.g. glucose) as well as waste (some salts, urea and excess water). The kidneys filter the blood but:

- reabsorb all the sugar
- reabsorb some salts (ions) needed by the body
- reabsorb the water needed by the body.

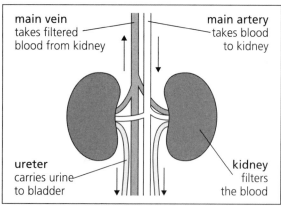

The control of water in the body

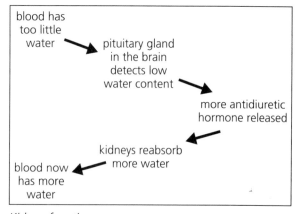

Kidney function

The filtered blood leaving the kidneys now contains only useful substances. The waste (urine) is drained from the kidneys by the ureter to the bladder.

How do the kidneys 'know' how much water to reabsorb? This is controlled by the pituitary gland in the brain.

Body temperature

This is controlled by a **thermoregulatory centre** in the brain. Sensory cells (receptors) are sensitive to the temperature of the blood flowing through the brain. Receptor cells in the skin also send messages to the centre. Most important is the core body temperature. This is the temperature in the central part of your body which contains the main organs.

Core temperature too high	Core temperature too low
blood vessels supplying capillaries in the skin dilate, so that more blood flows near the skin's surface and more heat is lost	blood vessels supplying the skin's capillaries constrict
sweat glands release sweat which uses the heat of the skin to evaporate, so cooling the body (we lose water through sweating)	muscles may 'shiver' – the respiration to provide the energy for this movement releases heat

Blood sugar level

The hormones **insulin** and **glucagon** control blood sugar levels. They are produced in the pancreas.

Sugar level too high	Sugar level too low
pancreas releases insulin into the blood – this makes the liver convert excess sugar to insoluble glycogen which is stored	pancreas releases glucagon into the blood – this makes the liver convert glycogen to glucose (sugar) which is released into the blood

Diabetes is a disease in which someone's pancreas does not produce enough insulin. Because of this the blood sugar level can rise too high and cause death. Diabetes can be controlled by a careful diet and by injecting insulin into the blood.

How do drugs affect our bodies?

Solvents, alcohol, tobacco and other drugs can harm our bodies.

- Solvents affect behaviour and may cause damage to lungs, liver and brain.
- Tobacco smoke can cause lung cancer, emphysema (lung disease) and disease of the heart and blood vessels.
- Alcohol affects the nervous system by slowing down reactions. This can lead to lack of self control, unconsciousness and possibly coma. It may also affect the liver and brain.

Questions

1 After playing a game of basketball you look bright red. How would you explain this?

2 On a hot day you do not produce much urine. How would you explain this?

3 Draw a spider diagram to show the different ways tobacco smoke can harm your body. Tobacco smoke should be at the centre of the diagram.

Disease

What causes disease? One of the main causes is when **microbes** (micro-organisms), such as certain **bacteria** and **viruses**, get into our body. These cause a whole range of illnesses, from the common cold to meningitis and AIDS.

Microbes

A bacterial cell has cytoplasm surrounded by a cell membrane. All of this is surrounded by a cell wall. It has no nucleus.

Usually the genes which allow a cell to reproduce and make copies of itself are in the nucleus. In bacteria the genes are in the cytoplasm.

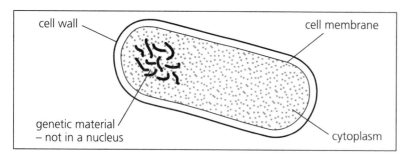

A bacterial cell

Viruses are much smaller than bacteria. They are very different to cells. They have a protein coat surrounding a few genes. They can only reproduce inside the living cells of other organisms.

A virus cell

If large numbers of microbes (bacteria or viruses) enter your body then you may catch a disease. The microbes can reproduce very quickly inside your body so that there are soon millions of them. They may produce **toxins** (poisons) which make you feel ill.

If a virus reproduces inside one of your cells the cell will be damaged.

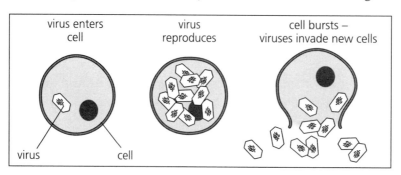

A virus reproducing

Defence against disease

The best defence is to stop the bugs getting in! Your body does this in several ways.

- Your skin acts as protection. If you have a cut microbes can get straight into your blood.
- Blood clots to form a scab. This seals cuts in the skin and stops microbes getting in.
- Air passages in your nose and lungs have a thick, sticky mucus on their surface inside to trap microbes. When you blow your nose or cough you are getting rid of these trapped microbes.
- Your stomach contains acid which can kill most microbes.

If the microbes get into your body then the white cells take action. They:

- ingest (eat) the microbes
- produce **antibodies** which help destroy particular microbes
- produce **antitoxins** to neutralise (get rid of) the poisons.

Once white cells have produced antibodies against a particular microbe then the next time the microbe enters your body they can produce the right antibodies more quickly. Your body is said to be **immune** to the microbe.

Disease and lifestyle

How do you come into contact with harmful microbes? There are two main ways.

- When ill people cough or sneeze they release a fine spray which contains microbes. If you breathe these in you risk catching the same illness.
- If you eat food prepared in unhygienic conditions or drink unclean water then you may become ill. Unclean water is often found when large numbers of people are crowded into one place without proper sewage treatment systems. Dirty water can carry cholera which spreads very fast and is very dangerous.

Questions

1 How are viruses different to other cells?
2 What are toxins and how does the body get rid of them?
3 If microbes do get into the body and disease results, what does the body do about it?
4 How are microbes prevented from getting into the body?
5 Sometimes in dense populations disease is able to spread very fast. Why is this?

Plant and animal cells

Like animals, plants are made up of cells. Plant and animal cells have the following parts:

- a **nucleus** controlling the cell
- **cytoplasm** where the chemical reactions take place
- a **cell membrane** allowing substances in and out.

Plant cells also have:

- a **cell wall** which maintains a rigid shape
- **chlorophyll** for photosynthesis (in **chloroplasts**)
- a **vacuole** containing cell sap.

Some cells are specialised to do certain work. Groups of cells with the same structure and function are called **tissues**. In plants, xylem cells make up **xylem** tissue which transports water. Different tissues make up an **organ** (e.g. a leaf).

A typical animal cell

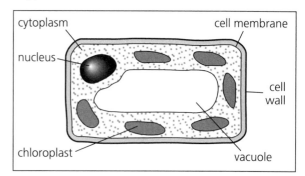

A typical plant cell

How do plants make their food?

Green plants make their food by **photosynthesis**. Light provides the energy for the process:

- green chlorophyll traps (absorbs) the light energy
- the energy is used to make glucose by combining carbon dioxide and water
- oxygen is released as a waste product

$$\textbf{carbon dioxide} + \textbf{water} \xrightarrow[\text{chlorophyll}]{\text{light energy}} \textbf{glucose} + \textbf{oxygen}$$

The rate of photosynthesis can be limited by:

- low temperature
- shortage of carbon dioxide
- too little light.

If you were growing lots of plants in a greenhouse it might be an idea to heat it. This would work as long as there was enough carbon dioxide and light getting into the greenhouse. If either light or carbon dioxide was in short supply you would be wasting your money because the plants couldn't photosynthesise any faster, no matter how much you heat the greenhouse.

Carbon dioxide

Carbon dioxide enters the plant through holes in the surface of the leaves, called **stomata**. It moves into the leaf by diffusion. It diffuses from a higher concentration of carbon dioxide in the air to an area of lower concentration in the leaf. Inside the leaf it also moves to the cells by diffusion.

Help

One stoma – many stomata.

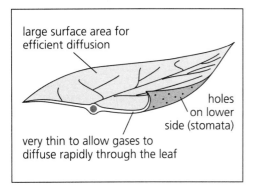

large surface area for efficient diffusion

holes on lower side (stomata)

very thin to allow gases to diffuse rapidly through the leaf

Structure of a leaf

more chloroplasts near top of leaf, to capture sunlight

waxy layer to reduce water loss

hole (stoma) to allow gases in and out of leaf

air spaces for gases to circulate

guard cell

carbon dioxide in

oxygen out (during photosynthesis)

Section through a leaf

Respiration

The glucose produced during photosynthesis can be stored as insoluble starch or used to release energy in respiration.

This energy can be used to build smaller molecules (particles) into larger ones for growth. Energy is used to change:

- sugars (glucose) into **starch** for storage
- sugars into **cellulose** for cell walls
- sugars, nitrates and some other nutrients into **proteins** for growth.

For healthy growth plants also need mineral ions taken from the soil through their roots:

- **nitrate** – makes proteins for growth
- **potassium** – helps the enzymes controlling photosynthesis and respiration
- **phosphate** – important in photosynthesis and respiration.

If a plant lacks some of these nutrients (ions) then the symptoms are shown in the table.

Nutrient lacking	Symptoms
nitrate	stunted growth with yellow, older leaves
phosphate	poor root growth and purple younger leaves
potassium	yellow leaves with some dead areas

Questions

1   Use a spider diagram to show all the parts a plant cell has that an animal cell does not have.

2   Why do lawns not need cutting in winter?

3   How does carbon dioxide get to the cells in a plant?

4   Give *three* uses for the sugars which plants produce.

5   A plant is not taking up enough phosphate. How could you tell by looking at it?

6   What is the equation for photosynthesis?

Transport in plants

Water

Plants take up water mostly through **root hair** cells on their roots. The root hairs provide a very large surface area for absorbing water.

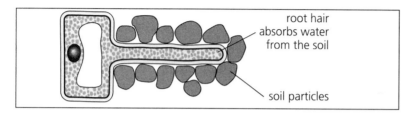

root hair
absorbs water
from the soil

soil particles

A root hair cell

Water is transported to all of the other cells in the plant. In flowering plants the **xylem** vessels transport water from the roots to the stem, leaves and other parts. **Phloem** vessels transport sugars from the leaves to all parts of the plant, but particularly to growing points and storage areas.

Osmosis

Water moves into the root hair cells by **osmosis**.

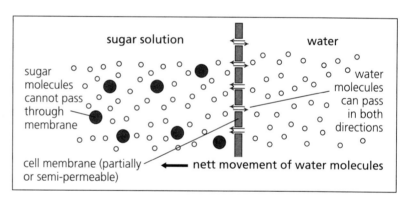

sugar solution

water

sugar molecules cannot pass through membrane

water molecules can pass in both directions

cell membrane (partially or semi-permeable)

nett movement of water molecules

You can see from the diagram that there is a greater concentration of water molecules to the right of the cell membrane (the part which is only water). There is a lower concentration of water molecules in the sugar solution. There is therefore a **concentration gradient** between the two. Water molecules will move both ways in a random way. However, more will move from the water to the sugar solution than the other way. We say that there is a **nett movement** from the water to the sugar solution.

Water helps to keep a plant upright. It enters the cells and makes them swell, or become **turgid**. A small seedling cannot stand up on its own without enough water – it **wilts**. However, plants do not want to take up too much water so they store the sugar they produce as starch – starch is insoluble and has no effect on osmosis.

Keeping the water

Plants lose water by evaporation from the leaves (**transpiration**). Much of this takes place through the stomata. If a plant loses more water than it can take up, it will wilt.

More water transpires on hot, dry, windy days.

Plants can reduce water loss by:

- closing the stomata – this is done by changing the shape of the guard cells which surround each stoma
- the waxy layer on the upper surface of plant leaves which stops too much water escaping. Plants which live in hot, dry conditions have a thicker waxy layer.

Active transport

Sometimes substances have to be absorbed into cells against a concentration gradient. For example, roots take up nutrients such as phosphates, nitrates and potassium from the soil where they may be in a more dilute solution than in the roots themselves. The plant uses energy to move them across cell boundaries against the concentration gradient.

How do plants respond?

Plants are sensitive to light, moisture and gravity:

- their shoots grow towards light and against the force of gravity
- their roots grow towards moisture and in the direction of gravity.

These responses are caused by **hormones**. Plants produce hormones which can collect unevenly in different parts. They will therefore cause uneven growth rates, which make the shoot or the root of the plant bend in the right direction.

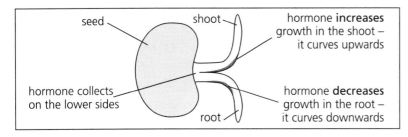

Plant hormone effects on a seedling

Plant hormones can be used to:

- help root cuttings to grow, so making large numbers of new plants quickly
- ripen fruit at the time the grower wants it to ripen
- kill weeds by making them grow so rapidly they die.

Questions

1 How are root hair cells adapted to maximise water uptake?

2 What is meant by the term 'osmosis'?

3 Use a spider diagram to show the different ways that humans use plant hormones. Put plant hormones at the centre of the diagram.

Why are we all different?

Differences in members of the same species are due to two quite different factors:

- the different **genes** that they have inherited (**genetic**)
- the conditions they have been brought up in (**environmental**).

Usually differences are due to a combination of these factors.

Genes

Genes are found within the nucleus of a cell. The nucleus contains **chromosomes** which are made up of many genes. Each gene controls some particular characteristic of the body (e.g. eye colour). The chromosomes are found in pairs. The number of chromosome pairs in body cells is different for each species. Human body cells have 23 pairs, making 46 chromosomes in all.

Both chromosomes in each pair are made up of genes which usually control the same characteristics. This means that the genes themselves are usually paired. Some genes have different forms – these are called **alleles**.

These alleles control the same characteristics but may carry different information about them. For example, in the pair of alleles controlling eye colour, there is one allele for blue and one allele for brown.

In sexual reproduction these chromosomes are regularly shuffled so that each individual has a unique combination of alleles.

Sexual reproduction

In sexual reproduction a male sex cell and a female sex cell join together. In humans these are the sperm and the egg. Sex cells are also called **gametes**.

Sex cells are formed by cells in the reproductive organs (ovaries and testes in humans) which divide to form cells which have one from each pair of chromosomes. This process is called **meiosis**.

Meiosis

Cells in the reproductive organs, as in the rest of the body, have one pair of each type of chromosome. At the start of meiosis a copy of each chromosome is made, so that there are two pairs of each.

The cell now divides twice to make four sex cells (see the diagram on the facing page). Each of these sex cells (gametes) has one copy of each chromosome.

When the male and female gametes join at fertilisation their single chromosomes combine, making a cell with its full number of chromosomes. New pairs of chromosomes and genes have been formed in the new cell, so that the new individual will be different.

Help

'Species' means a type of organism. Members of the same species can breed with each other.

Help

In humans:
- sperm = 23 chromosomes
- egg = 23 chromosomes
- baby = 46 chromosomes.

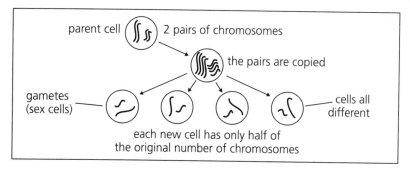

Cell division – meiosis

There is an almost infinite number of combinations of genes, and so an infinite number of possibilities for new individuals.

The new cell, formed when the gametes fuse, then divides again and again by **mitosis** to form a new individual.

Mitosis

Once the body is fully grown mitosis still takes place to replace cells which die. For example, skin cells are wearing off and being replaced all of the time.

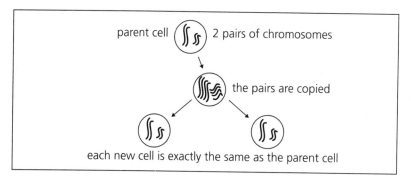

Cell division – mitosis

Mitosis is also the type of cell division used in asexual reproduction.

Asexual reproduction

No sex cells are involved in asexual reproduction, so the genetic information in the offspring is exactly the same as that of the parent. This type of reproduction is most common in plants (e.g. new plants growing from runners, tubers or bulbs). The offspring are called **clones**.

Help

In asexual reproduction new individuals are produced through mitosis.

Questions

1   What are the *two* factors causing variation between members of the same species?

2   How does a cell with 23 pairs of chromosomes divide to produce four new sex cells, with only half the number of chromosomes?

3   Why are organisms produced by asexual reproduction identical to the parent?

4   Turkeys have 82 chromosomes (in 41 pairs) in their cells. How many chromosomes do their gametes have?

Inheritance in humans

Determining sex

We have 23 pairs of chromosomes. One of these pairs determines the sex we are. In females the sex cells are the same (called XX because of their shape). In males they are different (called XY because of their shape). So eggs always have an X chromosome while sperm may carry an X chromosome or a Y chromosome.

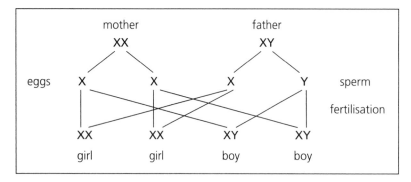

There is a 50% chance of having a boy and a 50% chance of having a girl

Inherited disorders

Some forms of disease are inherited:

- Huntington's chorea – a disorder of the nervous system
- cystic fibrosis – a disorder of the cell membranes
- sickle cell anaemia – a disorder of the red blood cells.

How are they inherited?

Like many of the other features of an individual, genetic disorders are controlled by pairs of genes. The genes in these pairs often have two alleles (alternative forms).

One of these alleles is the **dominant** form. That is, when it appears in the pair it determines the characteristic which that pair of genes controls.

For example, Huntington's chorea is controlled by a dominant allele (H) – if you have the allele you will develop the disorder. So it can be inherited from one parent who has the disorder.

The other allele is **recessive** (h). If it appears in a pair with the dominant allele, it does not control the characteristic linked to that gene. It is only when both alleles are recessive that their effects show.

For example, cystic fibrosis is carried only by recessive alleles (c), so both alleles must be recessive for the individual to develop the disorder. This means that both parents must carry the recessive allele.

If individuals have two identical alleles for a characteristic, whether these are dominant or recessive, they are said to be **homozygous** (e.g. cc). If they have a dominant and recessive allele, they are **heterozygous** (e.g. Hh).

 Help

You can use genetic diagrams to show the inheritance of dominant and recessive alleles clearly. The two alleles are shown by the same letter, but dominant alleles have a capital.

Worked examples

Q One heterozygous parent and one homozygous recessive parent for Huntington's chorea have a child. What is the chance of the child developing the disorder?

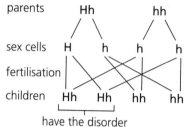

A The chance is one in two.

Q Two heterozygous parents for cystic fibrosis have a child. What is the chance of the child having cystic fibrosis?

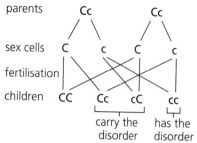

A The chance is one in four.

In sickle cell anaemia the disorder is carried by a recessive allele (s). Being heterozygous (Ss) helps to protect against malaria. This means that carrying the disorder can be an advantage in countries where malaria is common.

Worked example

Q Two parents who are heterozygous for sickle cell anaemia (so do not show symptoms) have a child. What is the chance that the child will develop the disorder?

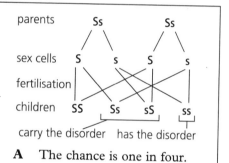

A The chance is one in four.

What are chromosomes?

They are long molecules of **DNA** (deoxyribonucleic acid). Genes are short lengths of DNA.

DNA contains the coded messages needed to produce certain proteins. It controls the order that amino acids are brought together to make these proteins.

The different proteins are responsible for the characteristics that we have.

Questions

1   One parent is heterozygous for sickle cell anaemia, the other homozygous (dominant). What is the chance of their children being carriers of the disorder? You should use a genetic diagram.

2   Two parents do not have Huntington's chorea. What is the chance, if any, of their children having the disorder?

Controlling reproduction

Artificial selection

We can choose those individuals with the best characteristics to breed from (e.g. the fastest male and female horses). This **selective breeding** is now a very big industry. A great range of plants and animals are being 'improved' in this way.

However, selective breeding reduces the variety of alleles in a population. This is because individuals without the alleles that are desired are not used to breed, so the alleles may eventually be lost.

It might be thought that this does not matter, but it does. The environment may change, new diseases may evolve and suitable alleles may not be there to help the species survive. For example, there may be alleles in a species which prevent a certain type of disease. If individuals are bred only for their meat or ability to produce milk, then some of these alleles may be lost along the way. It would then be difficult for the species to adapt to combat the disease should it break out.

As an alternative, modern **cloning** (a type of artificial selection) can involve:

- tissue culture – using small groups of cells from part of a plant to grow into a new plant
- embryo transplants – splitting cells from a developing embryo and transplanting into a 'host' parent (this must be done before the cells become specialised).

Genetic engineering

Genes from one species can be 'cut out' of a chromosome and transferred to another species (e.g. a bacterium). The transferred gene continues to make the same protein in its new 'home'.

On a large scale, the production of **insulin** is now carried out in this way by bacteria. They produce it for humans.

It is also possible to transfer genes to 'host' organisms at an early stage of development to give 'better' characteristics (e.g. genetically modified tomatoes).

How can women control their fertility?

An egg is released every month. The thickness of the lining of the womb (uterus) increases during the month. These changes are controlled by hormones secreted by the pituitary gland (at the base of the brain) and by the ovaries.

Fertility in women can be controlled by:

- hormones that stimulate (encourage) eggs to be produced (fertility drugs)
- hormones that stop eggs being released from the ovaries (the pill).

Help

The pill is the most reliable method of contraception, but for a few women can produce unpleasant side-effects such as giddiness, nausea or occasionally thrombosis (blood clots).

Several hormones are involved in the menstrual cycle. The hormones controlling egg release include:

- **follicle stimulating hormone** (FSH) secreted by the pituitary gland – this causes the eggs to mature and ovaries to produce oestrogens

- **oestrogens** now inhibit (stop) more production of FSH, which stops more eggs maturing

- oestrogens also cause the pituitary gland to produce luteinising hormone (LH)

- **luteinising hormone** causes the release of an egg mid-way through the cycle.

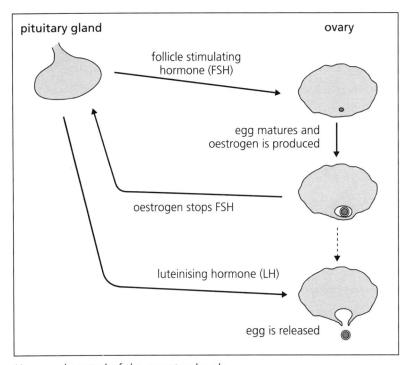

Hormonal control of the menstrual cycle

FSH can be used as a fertility drug if a woman's own production of FSH is too low. Oestrogen can be taken (as a pill) to stop FSH production so no eggs are released (birth control).

 ## Questions

1 Describe *one* example of genetic engineering.

2 A small animal in South America is near extinction. Scientists start a breeding programme using only the most attractive animals. The number of animals in the population rises. A disease strikes the population and the scientists prove helpless to save the animals, which then die out.
   Another scientist says that it was our fault the animal became extinct. How could she explain her statement?

3 What is meant by cloning? What type of cell division does it involve?

Natural selection

How do new species evolve?

Genes may change because of **mutation**. Mutations occur naturally but the chances of one can be increased by:

- exposure to ultraviolet light
- exposure to X-rays
- exposure to other forms of radiation
- exposure to some chemicals.

Most mutations are harmful:

- reproductive cells may become abnormal or die
- body cells may multiply out of control, and the effect may spread – this is **cancer**.

Some mutations have no effect and some may even *increase* the chance of survival.

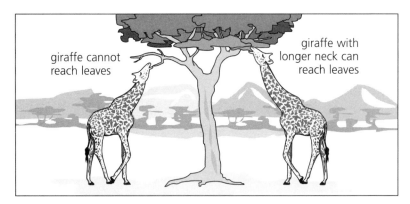

giraffe cannot reach leaves

giraffe with longer neck can reach leaves

A giraffe with a longer neck than the others may be able to find food more easily because giraffes feed from the leaves on higher branches of trees. The best adapted members of a species (e.g. giraffes with longer necks) are more likely to breed as they are more likely to survive. Over many generations this will result in small changes in the species. This is called **evolution**.

Evolution of a species occurs through **Natural Selection**.

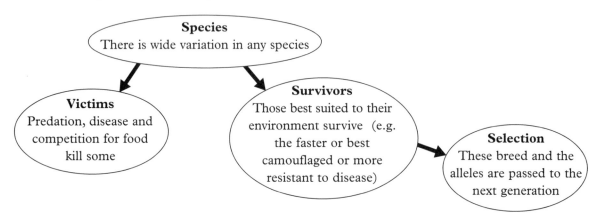

Species
There is wide variation in any species

Victims
Predation, disease and competition for food kill some

Survivors
Those best suited to their environment survive (e.g. the faster or best camouflaged or more resistant to disease)

Selection
These breed and the alleles are passed to the next generation

Faster antelopes get away

How do species die out?

Fossils are found in rocks. They are the remains of plants and animals that lived a very long time ago. They were formed:

- from the hard parts of animals which did not decay easily
- from other parts which did not decay because of lack of oxygen
- when parts of the organism were replaced by other materials as they decayed (e.g. chemicals may dissolve out of seashells and be replaced by minerals such as iron or silicon which then preserve the shape).

Fossils show us how species have changed over millions of years. We now know that all of the species today developed from simple life forms over three billion years ago.

Species become extinct:

- if their environment changes (e.g. change in temperature)
- if predators eat them all
- if disease kills them all
- if a new species successfully competes with them (e.g. takes all of their food source).

 Questions

1. Fully preserved specimens of insects which are thousands of years old have been found preserved in amber (solidified sap). Explain why they are so well preserved.

2. Give *three* different causes of mutation.

3. There are two varieties of peppered moth in Britain, pale and dark. Pale moths are found in rural areas where tree trunks are mottled grey. Dark moths are found in industrial areas where tree trunks are blackened. Suggest how this distribution might have come about.

4. Draw a spider diagram to show the different ways a species might become extinct. Extinction should be at the centre of the diagram.

Competition and survival

Organisms have features to help them survive in the places where they usually live. For example polar bears live in very cold areas and have very thick fur and a very thick layer of fat under their skin to help insulation. Holly leaves have a very waxy layer on the upper surface of their leaves to prevent too much water loss, especially in winter when the plant may not be able to take up very much water (as the water may be frozen).

Plants often compete with each other for:

- space
- water
- nutrients.

For example, a new seedling trying to grow underneath an oak tree is likely to die.

Animals often compete with each other for:

- space
- water
- food.

For example, birds all have their territories which they protect. This is so that they have space to breed and enough food to eat.

Animals which kill and eat other animals are called **predators**.

The animals they eat are called **prey**.

Help

Weasel – a predator
Mouse – prey

In a community of organisms:

- the animal **population** is usually limited by the amount of food (e.g. the number of foxes could be limited by the number of rabbits and other food that there is to eat)
- if the number of prey increases it is likely that the number of predators will also increase (e.g. if the number of voles increases then you might expect the number of local owls to increase)
- if the population of predators increases the number of prey is likely to decrease (e.g. if the number of owls increases then the number of voles is now likely to decrease).

The size of a population may be affected by:

- the total amount of food or nutrients available
- competition for food or nutrients
- competition for light
- predation or grazing
- disease.

Help

Population – the total number of that type of organism in an area (e.g. the number of badgers in a wood).
Community – all of the organisms living in a particular area (e.g. all of the organisms, including plants, living in a pond).

Food chains and webs

Radiation (light and heat) from the Sun provides the energy for plants – and therefore the animals which eat them. Green plants only capture a small part of the Sun's energy. The energy is then stored in the substances that make up the plant cells.

In nature it is very rare to have a simple food chain. A rabbit, for example, may eat grass but so do many other animals. A fox may eat a rabbit but so might weasels or buzzards.

If we connect up all the food chains then we create a food web, which gives us much more detailed information.

A simple food web

 Questions

1. Kestrels hunt for mice along the side of a road. What is the predator and what is the prey?

2. One year there are a lot of mice. What is likely to happen to the kestrel population? What is then likely to happen to the number of mice?

3. Draw a spider diagram to show the different factors which will affect the size of a population of animals. Animal population should be at the centre of the diagram.

4. On holiday you see a kestrel hunting for small birds and mice in the hedgerow. The mice are eating seeds from some flowers and the birds are eating berries from the hedge and some of the seeds. Draw a simple food web to show this.

Pyramids of number and biomass

Food webs and chains show us how energy and material is transferred from one organism to another. The numbers of organisms involved at each stage can be shown in a **pyramid of numbers**.

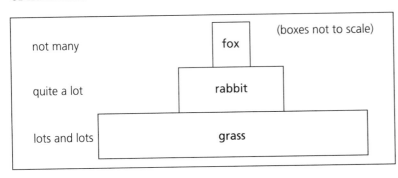

A pyramid of numbers

This pyramid shows the numbers of organisms supported in one community. Sometimes, however, a pyramid of numbers does not give a true picture of a food chain.

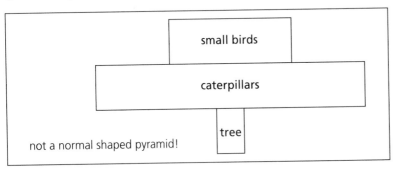

Another pyramid of numbers

A pyramid of numbers can be a strange shape if one of the organisms is large. A **pyramid of biomass** nearly always gives a good idea of the energy and material being transferred up a food chain. Biomass is the mass of living material in a community.

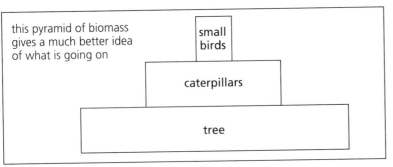

A pyramid of biomass

In the pyramids shown here, the tree is a single organism upon which many caterpillars can feed. If you consider its biomass you get a better idea of how much energy it supplies.

Losing mass through a food chain

It can be seen that as you go along the food chain less material (biomass) is contained in the organisms. There are a number of reasons for this.

All organisms use materials in respiration to release energy. The energy is used for growth and movement, and much is lost as heat to the surroundings or is excreted. Heat loss is particularly great in mammals and birds, whose bodies need to be kept at a constant temperature which is often higher than their surroundings.

The efficiency of food production (in other words, reducing losses) can be improved by:

- reducing the number of stages in the food chain (e.g. humans eating cereal grain is more efficient than feeding grain to cattle then eating the cattle)

- reducing the losses from animals by restricting their movement and controlling the temperature they are kept in (e.g. by keeping calves in crates to produce veal, the calves do not use up much energy in movement or by trying to keep warm).

This last point is, of course, a very contentious issue.

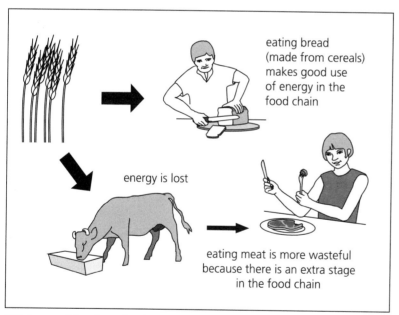

eating bread (made from cereals) makes good use of energy in the food chain

energy is lost

eating meat is more wasteful because there is an extra stage in the food chain

Efficiency of food production

Questions

1. Why does a pyramid of biomass usually give us more accurate information than a pyramid of numbers about what is happening to the energy in a community?

2. How is energy lost between the stages of a food chain?

3. Using a food chain, suggest *one* other example of a pyramid of numbers which does not result in a 'normal' pyramid shape.

What happens to the waste?

Microbes break down dead organisms, both plants and animals. This process of **decay** releases materials which can be used again by other living organisms. The materials are continuously recycled.

There are two important cycles that you must learn. These are the **carbon cycle** and the **nitrogen cycle**.

The carbon cycle

The carbon cycle

Use by living organism	How it is returned to the air
Plants use carbon dioxide in photosynthesis to produce carbohydrates, fats and proteins needed for plant bodies	Some carbon dioxide returns to the air from plant respiration
When animals eat plants, and these animals are eaten by other animals, the carbon becomes part of the carbohydrates, fats and proteins in animal bodies	Animals respire and return some carbon dioxide to the air
	When plants and animals die, their bodies are eaten by other animals or microbes which respire and release carbon dioxide into the air

The nitrogen cycle

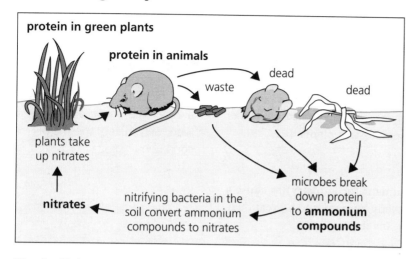

protein in green plants

protein in animals

dead

waste

dead

plants take
up nitrates

nitrates

nitrifying bacteria in the
soil convert ammonium
compounds to nitrates

microbes break
down protein
to **ammonium
compounds**

The nitrogen cycle

Use by living organism

Green plants take in nitrogen as **nitrates** from the soil

↓

The nitrates are used to make **proteins**

↓

As animals eat the plants some of the nitrogen becomes part of the animal's bodies

How it is returned to the soil

Nitrifying bacteria convert these ammonium compounds back into nitrates

↑

When the animals and plants die microbes break down the protein in them into **ammonium compounds**

Help

The full nitrogen cycle is very complicated. This is all that you need to know.

By the time all the protein has been broken down and recycled, all of the energy originally captured by green plants has been transferred.

If a community of organisms is **stable**, the processes of decay return as many materials (e.g. carbon and nitrogen) to living organisms as they need. The processes which use carbon and nitrogen are balanced by the processes which return them.

Questions

1 Copy and complete these sentences about the carbon cycle using words from the list. You will have to use one of the words more than once:

   respiring   decomposing   photosynthesising

   Carbon enters the carbon cycle through organisms which are _____. Organisms release carbon back into the cycle as they are _____. Dead, _____ organisms also release carbon back into the atmosphere as they are broken down by bacteria which are _____.

2 In what food types can carbon be found?

3 How is the nitrogen in animals and plants returned to the soil after the organisms have died?

How do humans affect the environment?

Acid rain

When we burn fossil fuels (e.g. coal, oil and gas) we release carbon dioxide and some sulphur and nitrogen oxides into the atmosphere. These gases can dissolve in rain and make it acidic. This rain may damage trees or fall into lakes and rivers. This may make the water too acid and as a consequence the animals and plants die.

Increase in population

In the past there were not enough humans (or industry) to cause a significant problem. Now there are many humans and a great deal of industry across the world. This means that:

- the Earth's raw materials, including fossil fuels (which are non-renewable) are being used up quickly

- we produce much more waste which, unless we deal with it properly, pollutes our surroundings.

Fertilisers

These are added to the land by farmers to replace the nutrients that plants take up for growth. However, some is washed into lakes, ponds and rivers by rain.

The fertilisers result in **eutrophication.** This means that:

- the water plants grow quickly

- some plants die as a result of increased competition (those below the surface may receive little light because of the large numbers growing on the surface)

- microbes (bacteria and fungi) break the dead plants down and use up the oxygen in respiration

- animals will die (suffocate) because of a lack of oxygen.

Help

Acid conditions can kill plants and animals because enzymes work only in very specific pH conditions.

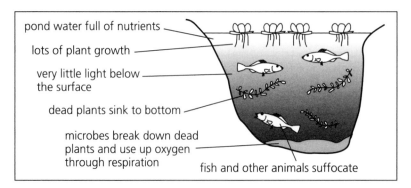

pond water full of nutrients

lots of plant growth

very little light below the surface

dead plants sink to bottom

microbes break down dead plants and use up oxygen through respiration

fish and other animals suffocate

Eutrophication in a pond

You might think that with so many plants photosynthesising there would be a lot of oxygen (as the waste product) for fish to use. However, it is all used up by the respiring microbes.

Untreated sewage in rivers and streams causes the same problem because the microbes break it down and use up the oxygen.

The Greenhouse Effect

Forests are being cut down. This is called **deforestation**. The wood may be used for timber and the land for agriculture. This has several results.

- If the wood is burned then carbon dioxide is released as a product of combustion.
- If the wood is left to decay then the respiring microbes release carbon dioxide.
- Fewer trees use less carbon dioxide to photosynthesise.

Carbon dioxide in the atmosphere is also released by the burning of fossils fuels (e.g. coal for power stations, petrol from oil).

Methane gas is released into the atmosphere by cattle farming and by rice fields.

The levels of these two gases are rising. They act like a blanket, trapping some of the Sun's energy which would normally be reflected back out of our atmosphere. So the temperature of the Earth increases. This is known as the 'Greenhouse Effect'.

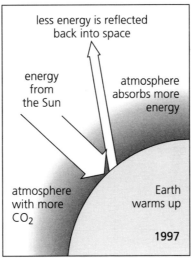

The Greenhouse Effect

A rise in temperature of a few degrees Celsius may cause:

- significant changes in the Earth's climate
- a rise in the level of the sea.

Questions

1 How can burning fossil fuels destroy life in a lake?

2 If too much fertiliser gets into a pond, why might all of the animals die?

3 Why is there more carbon dioxide in the air now than there was 100 years ago?

4 Why might the increasing amounts of carbon dioxide in the air cause the temperature of the Earth to increase?

Exam questions

1 The drawing shows the fossil remains of a bird that is now extinct.

a Suggest and explain **two** possible reasons why this bird became extinct. [2]

b The fossil is about 140 million years old. Describe what would have happened to the muscles and other soft organs of the body soon after the bird died. [4]

[Total 6]

2 The diagram shows the mean daily input and output of water for an adult.

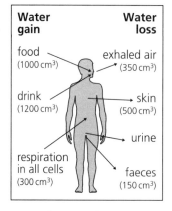

a Respiration is a source of water. Complete the equation for respiration:

sugar + _____
→ water + _____ + energy [2]

b The kidneys keep the water content of the body constant by controlling the volume of water passed out in the urine.

i Use data from the diagram to calculate the mean daily output of water in urine (in cm^3). Show your working. [2]

ii Describe how the amount of water in the body is controlled by the kidneys. [3]

[Total 7]

3 The wild turkey, which originated in America, weighs up to 6 kg. Wild turkeys have black feathers, sometimes with white edges or bars. Until about thirty years ago turkeys reared for meat also had black feathers, as shown.

However, a recessive gene appeared which produced entirely white feathers, and turkey farmers changed to breeding white-feathered birds.

Supermarkets preferred white-feathered birds because small pieces of feather left in the skin after plucking were not visible as dark patches. Customers wanted unblemished oven-ready birds. Now, however, there is a demand again for birds with black feathers, which can be marketed as 'traditional' farm-produced turkeys.

a Feather colour is controlled by one pair of genes.

i Suggest suitable symbols for **each** of the two alleles of this pair of genes. [1]

ii What alleles for feather colour would a white turkey have? [1]

iii Give **two** possible ways in which the mutant allele might have been produced. [2]

b Explain carefully why 'traditional' black-feathered turkeys could not be bred from a flock of white-feathered birds. [1]

c It is likely that white-feathered turkeys would be less suitable for selective breeding for other characteristics, such as size, than black-feathered birds. Suggest why this is so. [2]

d In the future, it might become possible to clone a particular variety of turkey by separating the cells in embryonic tissue. What might be the advantages and disadvantages of this technique? [5]

[Total 12]

4   Read the following passage, from an article in *Woman's Own*.

> ### One day I'll have to tell you ... but not now
>
> Sally has Huntington's chorea and knows she may have passed the deadly disease on to her son Peter.
>
> *You're seven now; and a beautiful little boy, but you know there's something wrong with me. I only hope that you won't suffer the same fate. My nightmare began nine years ago, on the day I announced to Nanny and Grandad – my mum and dad – that I was getting married. After I told them my happy news, they looked at me and said there was something important I should know. They told me that your Grandad had Huntington's chorea and there was a risk that I could have it as well.*

a   Give **two** symptoms of Huntington's chorea. [2]

b   There is no history of Huntington's chorea in the family of Peter's father.

 i What is the chance that Peter has inherited the disease? [1]

 ii Explain why. You may use a genetic diagram if you wish. [3]

[Total 6]

5   The table shows the amount of blood flowing through the lungs and the muscles when the body is at rest and during strenuous exercise.

	Volume of blood passing through organ (cm³/minute)	
	at rest	during vigorous exercise
Lungs	100	200
Muscles	750	12 500

a   Blood flows through capillaries in the lungs.

 i Give **two** changes in the composition of the blood as it flows through the lung capillaries. [2]

 ii Explain how the body makes more blood flow through the lungs during exercise. [2]

b   Explain, as fully as you can, the advantage to the body of increasing the amount of blood flowing through the muscles during exercise. [5]

[Total 9]

6   An oak wood contained the following:
   200 oak trees
   150 000 primary consumers
   120 000 secondary consumers

a   Draw and label a pyramid of biomass for **this** wood. (Your pyramid does **not** have to be drawn to scale.) [2]

b   A scientist estimated the total amount of energy flow through each level of the pyramid per year. The results were:

   Energy absorbed by oak trees
   4 600 000 kJ/m²/year
   Energy in sugar produced by trees
   44 000 kJ/m²/year
   Energy transferred to primary consumers
   2 920 kJ/m²/year
   Energy transferred to secondary consumers
   700 kJ/m²/year

 i Calculate the percentage of the energy absorbed by the trees that is transferred to sugar by photosynthesis. Show your working. [2]

 ii Suggest **two** reasons why a large proportion of the energy is not transferred to sugar. [2]

 iii Give **three** reasons why some of the energy in the primary consumers is **not** passed on to the secondary consumers. [3]

c   Conditions may change considerably during the course of a summer's day. Explain how different factors may determine the rate of photosynthesis at different times of the day. [3]

d   In autumn, the leaves fall from the oak trees. The leaves contain some proteins. Explain how the nitrogen in these proteins becomes available for the oak trees to use again. [4]

[Total 16]

7 Read the following passage, which is taken from an advice book for diabetics.

Insulin reactions

Hypoglycaemia, or 'hypo' for short, occurs when there is too little sugar in the blood. It is important always to carry some form of sugar with you and to take it immediately you feel a 'hypo' start. A 'hypo' may start because:
- *you have taken too much insulin, or*
- *you are late for a meal, have missed a meal altogether, have eaten too little at a meal, or*
- *you have taken a lot more exercise than usual.*

The remedy is to take some sugar. An insulin reaction usually happens quickly and the symptoms vary – sweating, trembling, tingling of the lips, palpitations, hunger, pallor, blurring of the vision, slurring of speech, irritability, difficulty in concentration. Do not wait to see if it will pass off, as an untreated 'hypo' could lead to unconsciousness.

a Many diabetics need to take insulin.

i Explain why.   [2]

ii Explain why there is too little sugar in the blood if too much insulin is taken.   [3]

iii Explain why there is too little sugar in the blood if the person exercises more than usual.   [3]

b Suggest why **sugar** is recommended for a 'hypo', rather than a starchy food.   [3]

c Explain how the body of a healthy person restores the blood sugar level if the level drops too low.   [3]

[Total 14]

8 The drawing shows a flamingo. Flamingos are birds which live in warm, shallow lakes in tropical Africa. Flamingos feed by sieving single-celled green algae and bacteria from the lake water.

a Lakes in tropical Africa support large numbers of flamingos. There would not be enough algae in a British lake to feed large numbers of these birds.

i Suggest **one** environmental factor that might account for the difference in the number of algae in African and British lakes.   [1]

ii Explain how this factor causes a difference in the number of algae in the lakes.   [2]

b In Kenya the large numbers of flamingos in one of the lakes, Lake Nakuru, is a big attraction to tourists. The Kenyan government wants to expand a nearby industrial town. One effect would be an increase in the amount of sewage that flows into Lake Nakuru.

i Suggest and explain how increasing amounts of sewage are likely to affect the organisms in the lake.   [4]

ii Suggest and explain why the Kenyan government wants to increase the size of the industrial town even though this might affect tourism in the area.   [3]

[Total 10]

9 Marathon runners are recommended to have a high carbohydrate diet prior to a race. Three athletes tried out three dietary regimes prior to a marathon race. The three dietary regimes were as follows.

Athlete A

Up to 7 days before race – Normal mixed diet
7 days before race –

Prolonged extreme physical activity
6–3 days before race –

Protein and fat diet; no carbohydrate
2 and 1 days before race –

Large carbohydrate intake

Athlete B

Up to 5 days before race – Normal mixed diet
5 days before race –

Prolonged extreme physical activity
4–1 days before race –

Large carbohydrate intake

Athlete C

Up to 4 days before race – Normal mixed diet
4–1 days before race –

Large carbohydrate intake

The graph below shows the effect of each of these dietary regimes on the glycogen levels in the athlete's muscles.

a i What is the immediate effect of extreme physical activity on the glycogen content of muscles? [1]

ii Describe how this effect occurs. [3]

b i Evaluate the three regimes as preparation for a marathon race. [3]

ii Suggest a possible explanation for the different effects of the three regimes. [2]

[Total 9]

10 The graphs show the results of an investigation into the control of sweating in humans. The subject was placed in a chamber where the temperature was maintained at 45 °C. The subject swallowed ice at the times indicated on the graphs.

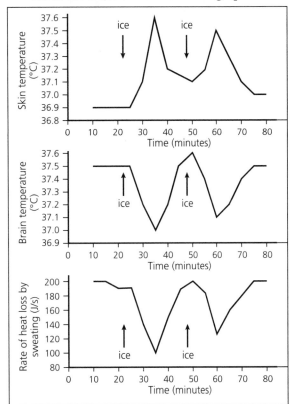

a What was the relationship between swallowing ice and the subject's

i skin temperature? [1]

ii brain temperature? [1]

iii rate of heat loss by sweating? [1]

b Explain, as fully as you can, why the subject's brain temperature, skin temperature and rate of heat loss by sweating were affected by swallowing ice in the way shown by the graphs. [8]

c The mammoth is an extinct relation of the elephant, which lived in arctic regions. The modern elephant lives in tropical areas. The mammoth, which was very hairy, and the elephant are both thought to have evolved from a scantily haired ancestor. Explain, as fully as you can, how the **mammoth** evolved from the common ancestor. [5]

[Total 16]

11   The drawings and text for this question are based on an article from *The Independent* newspaper.

corn cockle

pheasant's eye

shepherd's needle

corn gromwell

spreading hedge parsley   corn mouse tail

Some of Britain's rarest wild flowers are likely to make a comeback thanks to an EC set-aside regime in which 15 per cent of arable land has been taken out of production.

As a result of this set-aside, pheasant's eye, corn gromwell, corn cockle, spreading hedge parsley and corn mouse tail are now thriving once again. They were once common in and around cereal fields and were even regarded as weeds, but were swept to near extinction by the intensification of agriculture after the Second World War. Their small, pale flowers are hardly seen. These plants cannot compete in fields where modern cereal crops are cultivated. Nor, however, do they flourish in semi-natural or wild habitats where nature is left to its own devices. They need farmland which is lightly tilled and cut once a year.

Dr Nick Sotherton, lowland research manager with the Game Conservancy Council, says that these species will flourish under the new rotational set-aside regime, in which farmers are compensated for taking land out of production in an attempt to end crop surpluses.

EC agriculture ministers are meeting to decide how much land should be used for rotational set-aside – in which a field is taken out of production for just one year before being replanted – and how much should be set-aside permanently. The ultimate set-aside is a wood, and Britain is seeking a forestry option.

The Game Conservancy Council says that the rotational scheme can benefit ground-nesting birds as well as rare flowers that will not be helped by longer-term set-aside. But Richard Knight, of the Wildlife Advisory Group, says 'Non-rotational is better because it gives flora and fauna a chance to get well-established.'

'Intensification of agriculture' has led to the creation of artificial ecosystems.

a   Explain how the creation of artificial ecosystems may have led to the near-extinction of the plants illustrated.   [4]

b   What would you recommend to ministers meeting to decide a policy involving rotational set-aside and permanent set-aside? Explain the reasons for your answer.   [4]
[Total 8]

12 a Copy and complete the diagram below to show how the sex of a child depends on the chromosomes the child inherits.   [3]

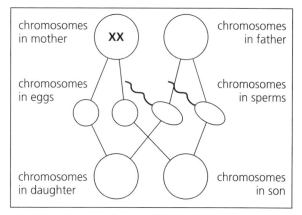

chromosomes in mother   **XX**   chromosomes in father

chromosomes in eggs   chromosomes in sperms

chromosomes in daughter   chromosomes in son

b   The diagram below shows the inheritance of Huntingdon's chorea in a family.

A B   **First generation** (all over 40 years old)

Second generation (all over 40 years old)

C D E F

Third generation (all under 30 years old)

G H

Key

■ male showing symptoms of Huntington's chorea
□ male without symptoms of Huntington's chorea
● female showing symptoms of Huntington's chorea
○ female without symptoms of Huntington's chorea

Symptoms of Huntingdon's chorea usually develop between the ages of 35 and 40. What are the chances that **G** and **H** will develop Huntingdon's chorea? Explain the reasons for your answers as fully as you can. You may use genetic diagrams if you wish.   [6]
[Total 9]

13 While preparing for a long race, athletes are advised to have a diet that consists mainly of carbohydrate before the race. The carbohydrate in the diet should be starch.

a Describe what would happen to the starch in the athlete's digestive system. [2]

b The graph below shows the effect of a high carbohydrate diet on the stored carbohydrate in the muscles.

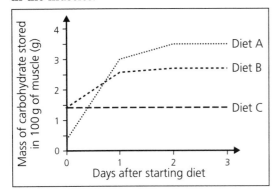

Diet A High carbohydrate diet, started after several days of eating a diet without carbohydrate.

Diet B High carbohydrate diet, started after a normal mixed diet.

Diet C Normal mixed diet.

What advice would you give the athlete about the best diet preparation for a long race? [2]

[Total 4]

14 The diagram below shows the mass of carbon involved each year in some of the processes in the carbon cycle.

a Complete the equation for plant respiration. [2]

□ + energy ⟶
carbon dioxide + □ + energy

b i Calculate the mass of carbon removed from the atmosphere each year. (Show your working.) [1]

ii Calculate the percentage of this total which is removed by the photosynthesis of land plants. (Show your working.) [2]

iii Calculate the net gain of carbon by the atmosphere in one year. (Show your working.) [2]

c As well as releasing carbon in carbon dioxide, combustion of fossil fuels releases pollutant gases into the atmosphere.

i Name **two** of these pollutant gases. [2]

ii Describe the effects of these gases on the environment. [2]

d Explain, as fully as you can, how the carbon in the bodies of dead organisms is returned to the atmosphere. [5]

[Total 16]

| Fossil fuels (5 billion tonnes) | Land plant respiration (50 billion tonnes) | Land plant photosynthesis (100 billion tonnes) | Deforestation by burning (2 billion tonnes) | Decomposition of dead organisms (50 billion tonnes) | Biological and chemical absorption (104 billion tonnes) | Biological and chemical emissions (100 billion tonnes) |

15 The diagram below shows a food web for a wood.

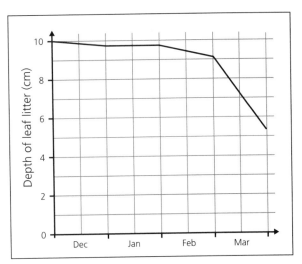

a Construct a food chain that contains **four** organisms including shrews. [2]

b Explain what would happen to the populations of small birds and moths if the gamekeeper succeeded in catching some of the weasels. [4]

c The diagrams below show a pyramid of numbers and a pyramid of biomass for 0.1 hectare of this wood.

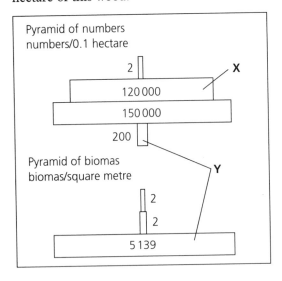

i Name **one** organism from the level labelled **X**. [1]

ii Explain, as fully as you can, why the level labelled **Y** is so much wider in the second pyramid than in the first. [3]

d A 1 m² area of the floor of the wood was fenced off so that animals could not reach it. The graph shows the depth of leaf litter inside the fenced area over the next few months.

i Explain, as fully as you can, why and how the leaf litter gradually disappeared. [2]

ii In which month does leaf litter disappear fastest? Explain why. [2]

iii Explain, as fully as you can, how nitrogen from the protein molecules in the leaf litter eventually becomes part of the protein molecules of new leaves. [6]

[Total 20]

Overall total: 162 marks

AT3

Materials and their Properties

Solids, liquids and gases

Matter can exist in three states – **solid**, **liquid** or **gas**. If you supply sufficient energy to a substance it may change from one state to another.

If you supply energy to a solid then the particles in the solid will vibrate more, and will therefore move more freely. Eventually the solid will melt. The temperature at which the state changes from solid to liquid is the **melting point**.

If you supply energy to a liquid then the particles will move around more quickly. If sufficient energy is supplied the liquid will boil – this is the **boiling point**. If more energy is supplied then the particles' attraction to each other will be overcome and some will escape from the liquid to form a gas. This is **evaporation.**

The particles of a gas move randomly in all directions. This is why gases spread out easily. This is known as **diffusion.**

What about dissolving?

The particles in a liquid move. If a solid is added to the liquid, the particles in the liquid may separate the particles of the solid from each other. This is **dissolving** (e.g. sugar in a cup of tea).

The three states of matter

Atomic structure

Everything we know is made from **atoms**. There are well over 90 different types of atom. A substance containing only one type of atom is known as an **element** (e.g. sodium, oxygen, hydrogen).

Atoms have a small nucleus containing protons and neutrons. Whizzing around this nucleus is a 'sea' of tiny electrons.

	Mass	Charge
proton	1	+
neutron	1	0
electron	negligible	–

In an atom there is always the same number of protons and electrons – resulting in no overall charge. All atoms of the same element have the same number of protons. The different elements have different numbers of protons. So:

• number of protons = proton number (or atomic number)

• number of protons + neutrons = mass number

In the periodic table the mass number and proton number are written at the top and bottom of the symbol for the element.

Example: mass number $^{23}_{11}\text{Na}$
             proton number

Sodium has therefore got:

• 11 protons

• 12 neutrons

• 11 electrons

Help

Atoms of the same element always have the same number of protons and electrons. They have no charge.

Isotopes

Atoms of the same element may have different numbers of neutrons. These atoms are called **isotopes** of the element (e.g. $^{35}_{17}Cl$ and $^{37}_{17}Cl$).

Electrons

Imagine that the electrons which orbit the nucleus are in different 'shells' (like layers in an onion). The shell nearest the nucleus can hold 2 electrons. The next three shells can hold 8 electrons. The shells are in fact **energy levels** (lowest energy nearest the nucleus). Electrons fill the lowest available energy levels, so they fill the shells closest to the nucleus. Atoms like to have full shells to make them stable. Noble gases have 8 electrons in their outer shells, so are very unreactive and stable.

You must be able to represent the atomic structure of the first twenty elements of the periodic table, using the periodic table in the data book. First you must work out the number of electrons and then place them in the shells. The first shell can take 2 electrons. The other shells take 8 electrons each. The last shell takes the number of electrons that are left.

Below is a diagram of an atom of sodium. It has 11 protons and 11 electrons. It therefore has no charge. The electronic structure of sodium can be written as 2, 8, 1.

Magnesium has an electronic structure of 2, 8, 2.

Help

An isotope is the same element but with a different number of neutrons.

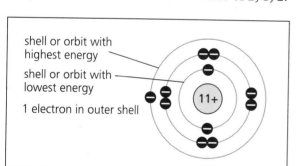

The electronic structure of a sodium atom

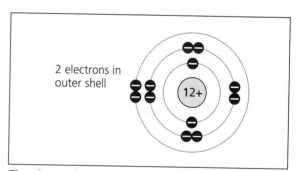

The electronic structure of a magnesium atom

Questions

1   A jug of water is left in the freezer. It turns to ice and you cannot pour it. When it melts you can pour the water. Explain what has happened.

2   Chlorine (Cl) has 17 protons. What is its electronic structure?

3   How many electrons does carbon ($^{12}_{6}C$) have in its outer shell?

4   Work out the electronic structure of magnesium ($^{24}_{12}Mg$), silicon ($^{28}_{14}Si$), argon ($^{40}_{18}Ar$) and oxygen ($^{16}_{8}O$).

Compounds

Ionic bonds

Most substances are compounds formed when two or more elements react and combine together. One way of forming a chemical bond is by losing or gaining an electron.

Look, for example, at the reaction between sodium and chlorine:

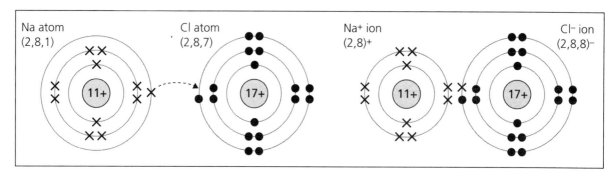

- Both elements now have a full outer shell of 8 electrons. They now have the electronic structure of noble gases.

- The sodium atom has lost one electron. It is now a positive sodium ion (it now has one more proton than it has electrons).

- The chlorine has gained one electron. It is now a negative chloride ion (it has one more electron now than it has protons).

The compound is sodium chloride (common salt). The bond between the two elements is an **ionic bond**. Ionic bonds are very strong. The compound is called an **ionic compound**.

Covalent bonds

Atoms can also form bonds by sharing electrons. These shared pairs are called **covalent bonds**. Atoms which share electrons often form molecules.

Some common covalent molecules

Help

'Dot and cross' diagrams often show only the outer shell electrons

When they are not in compounds, all of the elements which are common gases are found in diatomic molecules. This means molecules with two atoms (e.g. O_2, Cl_2).

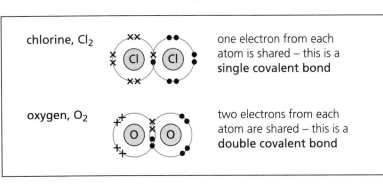

chlorine, Cl_2	one electron from each atom is shared – this is a **single covalent bond**
oxygen, O_2	two electrons from each atom are shared – this is a **double covalent bond**

Help

Some substances can exist in covalent *or* ionic forms. For example:

- hydrogen chloride can be HCl molecules or H^+ and Cl^- ions
- water can be H_2O molecules or H^+ and OH^- ions

The atoms in these molecules are more stable than the atoms on their own, because their highest energy levels (outer shells) are now full. Notice how oxygen (which has six electrons in its outer shell) needs to share another *two* electrons to make it stable – so forming a **double bond**.

Balancing chemical equations

The products made must have exactly the same atoms as the reactants, so:

Na(s) + **H₂O**(l) → **NaOH**(aq) + **H₂**(g)

1 sodium atom	1 sodium atom
2 hydrogen atoms	3 hydrogen atoms
1 oxygen atom	1 oxygen atom

not balanced

2Na(s) + **2H₂O**(l) → **2NaOH**(aq) + **H₂**(g)

2 sodium atoms	2 sodium atoms
4 hydrogen atoms	4 hydrogen atoms
2 oxygen atoms	2 oxygen atoms

equation now balanced

The letters (s), (l), (aq) or (g) following each reactant or product show the state of each substance.

State symbols	
s	solid
l	liquid
aq	dissolved in water (aqueous)
g	gas

Questions

1 Draw a diagram to show the electronic structure of $^{40}_{20}$Ca.

2 Predict how calcium will react with chlorine, in terms of the number of atoms reacting.

3 Show how you would represent a calcium ion.

4 Carbon dioxide has the formula CO_2. Draw a diagram of the molecule to show its covalent bonds. Write down *two* other ways of showing this bonding. (Atomic number of C = 6, O = 8)

Structure and properties

The structure of substances affects their properties. Ionic and covalent compounds, metals and plastics all behave in different ways which are related to their different bonding.

Ionic compounds

The ions of elements in an ionic compound have opposite electrical charges and so are held together strongly by forces of electrostatic attraction. Ionic compounds form regular structures (giant ionic lattices) in which each positive ion is surrounded by negative ions and each negative ion is surrounded by positive ions. This means that the whole lattice is held together strongly.

It is not easy to break this lattice by heating because a lot of energy is needed to pull the bonds apart. So ionic compounds have high melting and boiling points.

If, however, an ionic compound is melted or dissolved in water, the ions become free to move and will conduct electricity. So, for example, solid sodium chloride (common salt) does not conduct electricity but molten sodium chloride or a salt solution will.

sodium = ● chlorine = ○

The giant lattice structure of sodium chloride

Metals

Metals consist of giant structures in which the electrons from the highest energy level (outer shell) of each atom are free to move throughout the whole giant structure. The electrons:

- hold the atoms together in a regular structure
- allow the atoms to slide over each other
- allow the metal to conduct heat and electricity.

Covalent compounds

In compounds made of molecules there are strong covalent bonds between the atoms of the molecules but *not* between the molecules themselves. This means that the molecules can be pushed apart easily, and so substances made of molecules have low melting and boiling points.

There are one or two exceptions. Sometimes, covalent compounds take the form of giant lattices rather like ionic lattices. Examples are diamond and graphite (both forms of carbon) and silica (silicon dioxide).

Within diamond each carbon atom is covalently bonded to four other carbon atoms. This makes a rigid, giant covalent structure with high melting and boiling points. Silicon dioxide forms crystals of quartz with a 3D lattice similar to diamond. In graphite each carbon atom forms three covalent bonds with other carbon atoms and they form layers which are able to slide over each other.

The structure of diamond

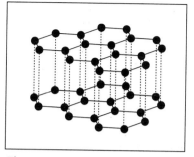

The structure of graphite

In covalent compounds the molecules have no charge because they are not made up of ions. Therefore, they cannot conduct electricity. Graphite is an exception to this because each carbon atom is only bonded to three others. This means that one electron in each atom is free to move around, and so graphite can conduct electricity.

Plastics are polymers. They are a tangled mass of very long molecules. The atoms in the molecules are joined by strong covalent bonds to form long chains.

In **thermosoftening plastic** the forces between the chains are weak. When the plastic is heated it goes soft. When it cools it goes hard again. These plastics are useful in industry when the plastic can be remoulded into various shapes during a manufacturing process. They are also useful if you need to add a colour (pigment) to the melted plastic before you let it harden. They are no use if the plastic object is going to be heated in the home (e.g. a dish for the oven).

Thermosoftening plastic

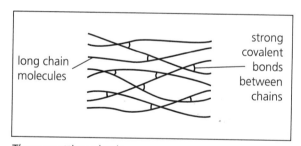

Thermosetting plastic

In a **thermosetting plastic,** once it has been heated and moulded and left to cool it will never soften again. The reason is that when the plastic has been heated new covalent bonds are formed between the chains alongside each other. These strong cross linkages prevent the plastic from softening again. The plastics cannot, therefore, be remoulded.

Questions

1 Why are molecular substances often liquids or gases at room temperature?
2 Diamond is so hard that it is used to cut other materials. Explain this in terms of its structure.

Crude oil and its products

Crude oil is obtained from the Earth's crust. It is formed from the remains of organisms which lived millions of years ago. Crude oil is a fossil fuel.

Oil, like coal and natural gas, is the result of heat and pressure (over millions of years and in the absence of air) on the remains of animals and plants trapped in sedimentary rock.

Oil and gas are less dense than water. They rise to the top of porous rock. They are then trapped below non-porous rock. We obtain the oil and gas by drilling down through the non-porous layer of rock.

Where to find oil

Help

Porous rock allows liquids to pass through it, like a sponge.

Crude oil is a mixture of very many compounds.

A mixture is made up of two or more elements or compounds which are not chemically combined together. This means that mixtures can be separated by physical processes. Oil is separated by **distillation** (it is heated and then the liquids that come off are condensed).

Fractional distillation

Most of the compounds in oil are made from hydrogen and carbon only, and so are called **hydrocarbons**. These different hydrocarbons can be separated by evaporating the oil and allowing it to condense at different temperatures. A different 'fraction' comes off at each temperature. Each fraction consists of one type of hydrocarbon which has molecules with about the same number of carbon atoms. This is known as **fractional distillation**.

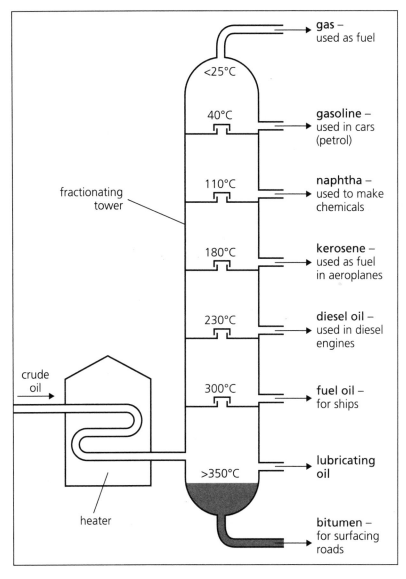

Fractional distillation

Hydrocarbon molecules in crude oil vary a great deal in size. The larger the molecules (which means that they have more carbon atoms) the:

- higher the boiling point of the hydrocarbon
- less volatile it is (this means it is more difficult to evaporate)
- less easily it flows (this means it is more viscous)
- less easy it is to ignite (this means it is less flammable).

Questions

1   Why do you find oil above porous rock and below non-porous rock?

2   Why can oil be split up into different compounds using physical processes?

3   Long-chain hydrocarbons are used to put the finishing surface on roads. Short-chain hydrocarbons are used as fuels. These hydrocarbons are never used the other way round. Explain why.

Alkanes, alkenes and polymers

Larger hydrocarbon molecules can be broken down ('**cracked**') to produce smaller, useful ones. Some are used as fuels and others to make plastics (polymers). Plastics include poly(ethene) and PVC:

- poly(ethene) (known as polythene) is used to make plastic bags
- polychloroethene (known as polyvinyl chloride or PVC) is used to make bottles, wellington boots and raincoats.

Carbon atoms form the backbone of hydrocarbon molecules.

When joined by single carbon–carbon bonds they are said to be **saturated**. These hydrocarbons are known as **alkanes**.

Help

Saturated means that the carbon atoms have no 'spare arms' to join with other atoms. In **unsaturated** hydrocarbons, one of the double carbon bonds readily breaks to join with other elements.

Ethane – an alkane

Others have double carbon–carbon bonds. These are **unsaturated** and known as **alkenes**. Some of the smaller molecules produced by 'cracking' are alkenes.

$$
\begin{array}{c}
H \quad H \\
| \quad | \\
H-C=C-H \qquad C_2H_4 \\
\end{array}
$$

Ethene – an alkene

The bonds are all covalent. This means that:

- the electrons are shared
- molecules are formed and not ions.

Unsaturated hydrocarbons are very reactive and can be used to make many useful substances including **polymers**. These are very large molecules formed from small molecules called **monomers**. When unsaturated monomers join together to make a polymer (with no other substances produced in the reaction) the process is known as **addition polymerisation**.

The way an addition polymer is formed can be shown like this.

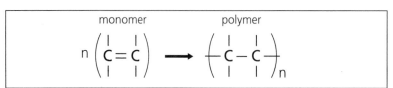

Addition polymerisation

Plastics are polymers. For example poly(ethene) is made from ethene.

monomer	polymer
H H | | C = C | | H H ethene	H H H H H H | | | | | | — C — C — C — C — C — C — | | | | | | H H H H H H poly(ethene) – commonly called **polythene**

Formation of polythene

PVC is not made simply from hydrogen and carbon. As the name polyvinyl chloride suggests, chlorine is involved.

monomer	polymer
Cl H | | C = C | | H H chloroethene	Cl H Cl H Cl H | | | | | | — C — C — C — C — C — C — | | | | | | H H H H H H polychloroethene or **PVC** (polyvinylchloride)

Formation of PVC (polychloroethene)

Polystyrene is a hard, brittle plastic used for making food containers such as yoghurt cartons. If you blow air into the plastic you make polystyrene foam which is used for packaging (e.g. for electrical equipment).

H   H   H   H   H   H   H   H
\| \| \| \| \| \| \| \|
C = C   ⟶   — C — C — C — C — C — C —
\| \| \| \| \| \| \| \|
H   ⬡   H   ⬡   H   ⬡   H   ⬡
styrene   polystyrene

You do not need to know the polymerisation reactions resulting in PVC and polystyrene. They are shown as examples of addition polymerisation.

Questions

1 Why are unsaturated hydrocarbons so reactive?

2 Why are large hydrocarbons 'cracked'?

3 Used plastic bottles cause a litter problem. One suggestion is to burn them all. Why might this not be such a good idea?

The effects of burning fuel

Burning

Burning is also known as **combustion** and is a very common type of chemical reaction. Burning produces new substances, mostly gases. When fuels burn they react with oxygen from the air. Oxidation has occurred. When a substance is burned in oxygen its elements are changed into oxides.

Most fuels contain carbon and/or hydrogen. Some also contain sulphur. The gases produced when they burn might include:

- carbon dioxide, CO_2 (from the burning of carbon)
- water vapour, H_2O (from the burning of hydrogen)
- sulphur dioxide, SO_2 (from the burning of sulphur).

There are increasing levels of carbon dioxide as a result of burning fossil fuels. The gas traps energy from the Sun in our atmosphere. The atmosphere therefore warms up (the **Greenhouse Effect**). Carbon dioxide is therefore known as a 'Greenhouse' gas.

Burning fuels results in high temperatures. This may cause nitrogen and oxygen in the air to combine and form nitrogen oxides.

Sulphur dioxide and nitrogen oxides produced by furnaces and car engines may dissolve in rain making the rain acidic. Lakes and rivers may become so acidic that living things can't survive. **Acid rain** also damages the stonework and metalwork on buildings.

Polluting gases

The atmosphere

For the last 200 million years the atmosphere has been made up of:

- about 80% nitrogen
- about 20% oxygen
- small amounts of other gases (e.g. carbon dioxide, water and the 'noble' gases).

This is very different to the Earth's atmosphere 1 billion years ago, which was more like the atmosphere of Venus and Mars today. The atmosphere then was formed by a lot of volcanic activity and contained:

- water vapour
- carbon dioxide
- small amounts of methane
- small amounts of ammonia
- little or no oxygen.

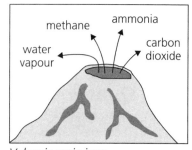

Volcanic emissions

As the Earth cooled, water vapour condensed to form the oceans.

As green plants evolved, the atmosphere started to change.

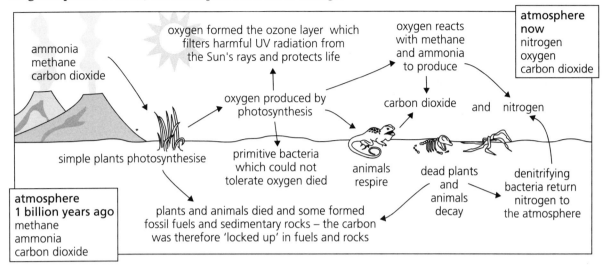

These changes in the atmosphere over 200 million years ago made it possible for new organisms to evolve and survive. There was:

- oxygen for the plants and animals to respire
- less methane which could kill them
- less ammonia which could kill them
- less carbon dioxide.

Primitive micro-organisms which had existed in the oxygen-free atmosphere could not tolerate the oxygen so died out.

Releasing carbon dioxide

Carbonates are sometimes moved deep into the Earth as a result of geological activity. If volcanic activity breaks them down, they release carbon dioxide back into the air. In addition we burn fossil fuels, releasing carbon dioxide which has been locked up for millions of years. This fast release increases the amount of carbon dioxide in the atmosphere.

The Earth can re-absorb carbon dioxide in the oceans. Carbon dioxide reacts with sea water to produce insoluble carbonates which are deposited as sediment and soluble hydrogen carbonates which remain in the sea. When there is too much carbon dioxide in the atmosphere this reaction increases, but even so the oceans cannot take all the increase in atmospheric carbon dioxide.

Questions

1 Why is the problem of acid rain increasing?

2 Explain how the amount of nitrogen gas has increased in the atmosphere over the last billion years.

3 Millions of years ago we could not have survived on Earth because of the atmosphere. Now we do survive. What changes in the atmosphere have taken place which allow us to survive?

Metals and their uses

Properties of metals

Metals have properties which non-metals do not have. More than 75% of the elements are metals (e.g. iron, magnesium, sodium).

Metals:

- are solid at room temperature (except mercury)
- have high melting points
- are shiny (when freshly cut)
- form alloys (mixtures of metals)
- are mostly strong and tough and can be hammered or bent into shape
- are good conductors of heat and electricity (whether solid or liquid).

Some common uses

Name	Alloys	Properties	Uses
iron		strong and tough can be bent into shape	cars bridges
copper		good conductor of electricity good conductor of heat can be bent into shape easily shaped	electrical wiring saucepans water pipes
	bronze		ornaments
aluminium	duralumin, with small amount of copper	strong easily shaped low density	aircraft manufacture

Which metals are the most reactive?

We can tell by looking at how quickly they react:

- with air to produce metal oxides, e.g.

    magnesium + oxygen → magnesium oxide
    $$2Mg + O_2 \rightarrow 2MgO$$

- with water (cold, hot or as steam) to produce metal hydroxides or oxides and hydrogen, e.g.

    calcium + water → calcium hydroxide + hydrogen
    $$Ca + 2H_2O \rightarrow Ca(OH)_2 + H_2$$

- with dilute acids to produce metal salts and hydrogen, e.g.

    zinc + hydrochloric acid → zinc chloride + hydrogen
    $$Zn + 2HCl \rightarrow ZnCl_2 + H_2$$

Help

The test for hydrogen is that it burns with a 'squeaky' pop.

The most reactive metals are at the top of the reactivity list. A more reactive metal will displace a less reactive metal from its compounds.

For example, aluminium is more reactive than iron so ...

aluminium + iron(III) oxide → iron + aluminium oxide
$$2Al + Fe_2O_3 \rightarrow 2Fe + Al_2O_3$$

The reactions help us to complete a **reactivity series**.

You do not need to know this diagram.

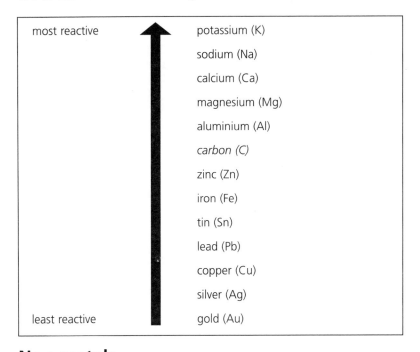

Some metals in order of reactivity

Non-metals

Less than 25% of the elements are non-metals.

Non-metals:

- mostly have low melting and boiling points – most are gases at room temperature
- are mostly dull in appearance
- are mostly brittle and crumbly when solid
- are mostly poor conductors of heat and electricity – whether solid or liquid.

Questions

1   Zinc is added to copper chloride solution. Predict and explain what would happen.

2   Metals have a number of properties. Draw a spider diagram to show *four* of these properties. Properties of metals should be at the centre of the diagram.

3   Mercury is a good conductor of electricity. Why is it never used for electrical wires?

4   What is the test for hydrogen gas?

Extracting metals from their ores

The more reactive the metal, the more difficult it is to extract it from its ore. This is because it readily forms strong compounds with other elements. Gold is so unreactive that it is found as a pure metal – there is no need to extract it. Most metals are more reactive.

The Earth's crust contains metals and metal compounds. They are usually mixed with other substances. There must be enough metal in the ore to make it worthwhile extracting it.

The ore is often a metal oxide, or something that is easily changed into a metal oxide. The oxygen, therefore, must be removed to leave the metal. This is known as a **reduction**. The more reactive the metal, the more difficult it is to remove the oxygen.

Extracting iron

Iron is less reactive than carbon so the following reaction is possible:

iron oxide + carbon → iron + carbon dioxide

The reaction takes place in a blast furnace.

The reaction in the blast furnace takes place in stages:

- coke (carbon) + hot air (oxygen) → carbon dioxide
- coke + carbon dioxide → carbon monoxide
- iron oxide + carbon monoxide → iron + carbon dioxide
  (a reduction reaction)

Acidic impurities go to the bottom of the furnace as waste. Limestone is added and reacts with the impurities to produce molten **slag**.

The blast furnace

Extracting more reactive metals

Many metals are more reactive than iron. It takes more energy to extract them from their ores. Aluminium is more reactive and must be extracted by **electrolysis**.

Most reactive metals form ionic compounds, where the metals are positively charged ions. When ionic compounds are either dissolved in water or melted, they can be broken down by passing an electric current through them.

When dissolved or melted the ions are free to move about. In electrolysis the positive ions are attracted to the negative electrode (cathode) and the negative ions are attracted to the positive electrode (anode). During this process gases can be given off or metals deposited on the electrodes.

Help

Electrolysis can only take place if the substance is ionic and the ions are free to move.

Extracting aluminium

The raw materials for producing aluminium are purified aluminium oxide and cryolite. Aluminium oxide has a very high melting point, so it is dissolved in molten cryolite at a much lower temperature.

The electrodes are made of carbon. During electrolysis:

- aluminium forms at the negative electrode
- oxygen forms at the positive electrodes where it reacts with the carbon to produce carbon dioxide – this makes the electrodes burn away quickly, so they have to be replaced frequently.

Extracting aluminium by electrolysis

Purifying copper

Electrolysis can also be used to purify copper.

Copper ions move from the impure copper positive electrode (anode) through a solution containing copper ions to the pure copper negative electrode (cathode). Here they are deposited as pure metal. So the positive electrode gets smaller and the negative electrode grows.

Purifying copper by electrolysis

Questions

1   Why is limestone added in the extraction of iron?

2   Why is carbon *not* used in the extraction of aluminium?

3   Why does the aluminium ore have to be melted before aluminium can be extracted? Why is cryolite used?

Structure of the Earth

The Earth is nearly a sphere. It has a layered structure, which includes:

- a thin **crust**
- an extremely viscous (thick liquid) **mantle** which goes almost half way to the Earth's centre
- a central **core** – made of nickel and iron, the outer part is liquid and the inner part solid.

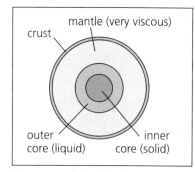

Structure of the Earth

The overall density of the Earth is greater than the densities of the rocks in the crust. This means that the inside is made of a material different from the rocks of the crust. It also means that the inside of the Earth must be denser than the rocks of the crust.

Continental crustal (granitic) rocks have slightly lower densities than oceanic crustal (basaltic) rocks, which is why they project above sea level.

It used to be thought that as the Earth cooled its circumference became smaller, and that this 'shrinking' forced rocks upwards to become mountains. We now know that this is not what happened.

The edges of continents are sometimes separated by thousands of kilometres of ocean. It seems that their shapes could fit together quite well (e.g. South America and Africa). They also seem to have similar patterns of rocks and fossils. This suggests that they were once joined together and have moved apart over millions of years.

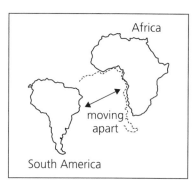

Continental drift

Plates and polarity

The Earth's crust is split into a number of very large pieces – rather like a jigsaw. These pieces are called **tectonic plates**. They are moving by a few centimetres every year, because they 'float' on the underlying mantle. This is slowly moving due to convection currents created by radioactive processes deep within the Earth.

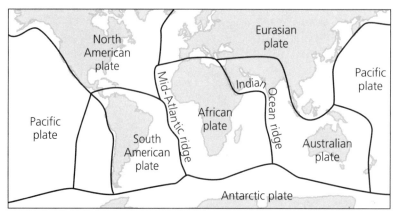

Tectonic plates

You do not need to know this map.

Tectonic plates may:

- slide past each other and cause earthquakes (e.g. San Francisco in California)

- move towards each other – the denser oceanic plate is driven down (subducted) beneath the thicker continental plate where it melts, helping to form a layer of molten rock called **magma**. Continental crust is forced upwards. Earthquakes result and magma may rise to form volcanoes (e.g. the Andes in South America)

- move apart and magma rises to fill the gap – new oceanic crust results. This is known as sea-floor spreading. The mid-Atlantic ridge is a good example.

Sea-floor spreading

As the magma spreads on the sea floor the iron-rich minerals line up in the direction of the Earth's magnetic field. The polarity or direction of the Earth's field reverses every half million years or so. The iron-rich minerals align themselves with whatever direction the field takes at the time. The magma cools to form stripes alongside the ridge. By studying the patterns of these stripes we can see how the sea floor has spread and how the Earth's magnetic field has changed over time.

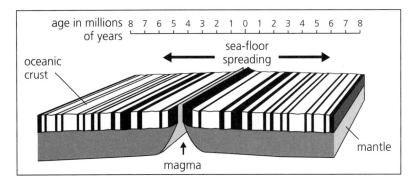

Magnetic stripes on the sea floor

Questions

1 What evidence is there that continents are moving apart?

2 In 1906 there was a disastrous earthquake in San Francisco. Recently there was a significant earthquake in Los Angeles. There are no mountains particularly near these two cities. What do you think caused the earthquakes?

3 How do the magnetic stripes on the ocean bed provide some proof that the sea floor is spreading?

Rock types and their formation

Igneous rocks

These are formed from molten rock (magma) in different ways.

- If molten rock is forced from inside the Earth up into the crust (but not onto the surface) it then cools and forms **intrusive** igneous rock (e.g. granite).

- If the molten rock erupts onto the surface (e.g. from a volcano) it forms **extrusive** igneous rocks (e.g. basalt).

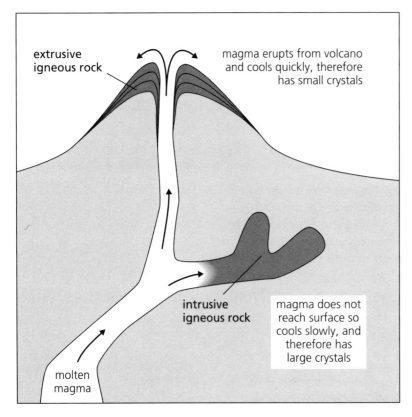

Igneous rock formation

Rocks composed of randomly arranged interlocking crystals (of a number of different minerals) are likely to be igneous. If the molten rock cools quickly (e.g. from a volcano) the crystals will probably be small. If molten rock cools slowly (e.g. below the Earth's surface) larger crystals are likely to be formed.

Sedimentary rocks

These were formed from layers of sediment deposited on top of one another on the sea floor. The weight of sediment squeezes out the water and it becomes cemented together, with other fragments, by salts crystallising out of the water. The process often takes millions of years.

These rocks include sandstone (made of grains of sand) and limestone made from calcium carbonate (often from shell remains of living organisms).

Sedimentary rocks usually lie on top of older rocks. These rock layers can be:

- tilted
- folded
- fractured (faults)
- and sometimes turned upside down!

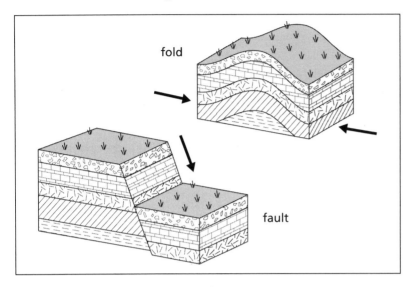

Movement of sedimentary rock

These Earth movements are caused by very large forces. Over a long time, the movements cause new mountain ranges to form (e.g. the Alps are great fold mountains formed when Africa collided with Europe). New mountains replace older mountains which have been worn down (eroded) by the weather.

Metamorphic rocks

These are often found in present-day and old mountain ranges. They are formed when there is a high temperature and pressure, often caused by the mountain building process. Metamorphic rocks are igneous or sedimentary rocks which have been buried underground by Earth movements. They become compressed and heated. Their texture may change without the rock melting.

Marble can be formed in this way from limestone. Shale can be formed from mudstone.

Rocks composed of bands of interlocking crystals are likely to be metamorphic. Schist is a good example.

Questions

1. How could sedimentary rock become magma?
2. You find a piece of granite. What type of igneous rock is granite and what size are the crystals likely to be?
3. Why do you think that metamorphic rocks are normally associated with mountain ranges?

Rocks and their uses

The rock cycle

The crust of the Earth is moving all the time. This results in changes which include some mountains being formed and others being worn away. The formation and transformation of different types of rocks can be summarised in the rock cycle:

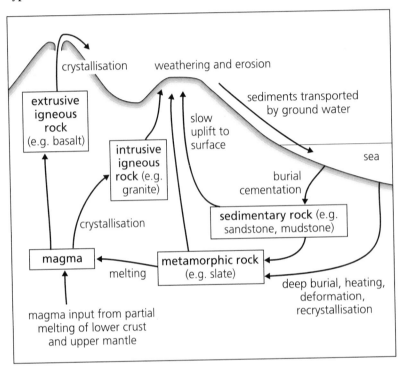

The rock cycle

The rock cycle takes place continuously but is, obviously, very slow.

As part of the rock cycle:

- sedimentary rocks may become metamorphic if they are put under sufficient heat and pressure
- metamorphic rocks may become igneous if they are buried and melt
- metamorphic rocks may become sedimentary if they are worn away and redeposited
- igneous rocks may become sedimentary if they are worn away and redeposited.

 Help

Remember: the faster an igneous rock cools, the smaller the crystals.

Using limestone

Limestone, a sedimentary rock, is mainly calcium carbonate. It can be quarried and used as a building material. Powdered limestone can be used to neutralise acidity in lakes and soils.

If you heat limestone in a kiln then **quicklime** is produced (calcium oxide). This reacts with water to produce **slaked lime** (calcium hydroxide) which reduces soil acidity.

Cement is made by roasting powdered limestone with powdered clay. If it is mixed with water, sand and crushed rock then a slow chemical reaction produces a hard, stone-like building material called **concrete**.

Glass is made by heating a mixture of limestone, sand and soda (sodium carbonate).

Using fossils

Sedimentary rocks often contain fossils. These are formed when the sediment is laid down and parts of plants and animals are trapped and preserved in the rock. Each layer of rock therefore contains fossils of the same age.

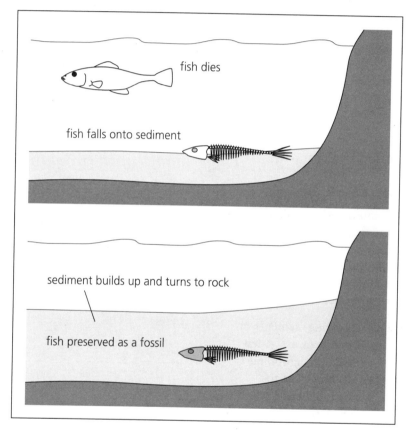

fish dies

fish falls onto sediment

sediment builds up and turns to rock

fish preserved as a fossil

Fossil formation

Fossils can therefore be used to identify rocks of the same age in different areas. They cannot be used to date rocks accurately, but they can be used to establish if rocks are younger or older than each other.

Questions

1 How might an igneous rock eventually become a metamorphic rock?

2 Fossils are being discovered every day yet they have been there for a very long time. Suggest *two* reasons to explain why they are continually being found.

3 Why do you not find fossils in either igneous or metamorphic rocks?

The periodic table

The elements can be arranged in order of their proton (atomic) number. This means that they are also arranged in terms of their electronic structure.

This list can then be arranged so that elements with the same number of electrons in their outer shells are in the same columns or groups. So, for example, the elements in group 1 (e.g. lithium, sodium, potassium) all have only 1 electron in the outer shell. These groups are like families of similar elements.

Part of the periodic table, showing the first 20 elements

The history of the periodic table

For a long time chemists searched for patterns which might explain and predict the behaviour of elements. Around 1800, John Dalton introduced the idea that chemical elements were made up of atoms, and that atoms of different elements but with similar properties could be grouped into threes or triads (e.g. lithium, sodium and potassium, which are all soft reactive metals).

In 1863 Newlands introduced the idea of arranging elements in order of their atomic masses in groups of eight (octaves). A few years later Mendeléev published the first clear table, grouping elements by their atomic mass *and* properties. Not all of the elements were known at the time, so this early table had gaps. When the elements were eventually found which fitted the gaps, it strengthened the idea of the periodic table.

Group 1 elements

These are called the alkali metals, because when they react with water an alkaline solution is produced. The alkali metals:

- are soft metals

- react with non-metals to form ionic compounds

- form ions that usually carry a 1^+ charge (as they lose their outer electron)

  $$2Na + Cl_2 \rightarrow 2Na^+Cl^-$$

- react with water releasing hydrogen and forming an hydroxide which dissolves in the water to form an alkaline solution

  $$2Na + 2H_2O \rightarrow 2NaOH + H_2$$

When placed in cold water, alkali metals float and may well move around on the surface. The more reactive the metal, the more vigorous its reaction with water.

The further down a group the metal is:

• the more reactive it is
• the lower its melting and boiling point.

So, potassium is more reactive than sodium, which is more reactive than lithium.

Why do these metals have different levels of reactivity, given that they all have 1 electron in the outer shell?

The answer is that the higher the proton number (and so the number of electrons), the further the outer electron is from the nucleus. It is at a higher energy level. The further away from the nucleus, the:

• more easily the electron is lost
• less easily electrons are gained.

The electronic structure of lithium is: 2, 1
The electronic structure of sodium is: 2, 8, 1
The electronic structure of potassium is: 2, 8, 8, 1

Group 0 elements (noble gases)

These are sometimes called group 8 elements as they have 8 electrons in their highest energy levels. The noble gases:

• are very stable (unreactive)
• all exist as individual atoms, not as molecules like other gases
• are used to replace air inside light bulbs (because oxygen in air *is* reactive, and would cause the filament to burn away).

Noble gases include helium, neon and argon.

Transition metals

These elements are in the centre block of the periodic table. Examples are iron (Fe) and copper (Cu). These metals:

• have high melting points
• are often used as catalysts (e.g. iron in the Haber process)
• form coloured compounds (e.g. iron oxide, which is red).

 # Questions

1 You may have seen sodium and potassium react with water. Both are very reactive but potassium is noticeably more reactive than sodium. Explain this in terms of its structure.

2 Why are group 1 metals often called 'alkali' metals?

3 Why are the noble gases so unreactive?

4 Xenon exists as atoms. Chlorine is a molecule and is diatomic. What do these statements mean?

The halogens

The halogens are the elements in group 7 of the periodic table.
They are called the halogen gases.

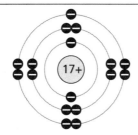

chlorine (2,8,7)
3 energy levels – outer shell
is of higher energy electrons

fluorine (2,7)
2 energy levels – easier for
electrons to join, so the atom
is more reactive than chlorine

Halogens:

- have 7 electrons in the outer shell and so need gain only
  1 electron to react
- if they react the halogen ion (halide) has a 1⁻ charge
- are non-metals
- have coloured vapours (e.g. chlorine is green)
- consist of molecules which are made up of pairs of atoms
  (e.g. chlorine Cl_2, bromine Br_2)
- form ionic salts with metals (e.g. potassium chloride,
  calcium bromide)

The further down the group you go the:

- less reactive the gas
- higher the melting and boiling points.

Halogens are less reactive as you go down the group. This is
because bigger atoms have more electrons, which occupy higher
energy levels. Extra electrons need to have sufficient energy to fill
the highest energy level (outer shell). This means that the atoms
find it increasingly difficult to accept electrons to make ions.

The order of reactivity (from highest to lowest) is: fluorine,
chlorine, bromine, iodine.

A more reactive halogen gas can displace a less reactive halogen
from an aqueous solution of its salt. For example:

$$2NaI + Cl_2 \rightarrow 2NaCl + I_2$$

The chlorine is more reactive than the iodine.

Metal–halogen compounds

Sodium chloride is a metal–halogen compound. It is common
salt and is found in large quantities in the sea and underground
(salt mines).

It can be broken down, when in solution, by electrolysis. This is an
important industrial process.

Help

Sodium (a reactive metal) reacts
with *chlorine* (a reactive non-
metal and poisonous gas) to
produce *sodium chloride*
(common salt) which you put
on your fish and chips!

Chlorine gas is formed at the positive electrode (chloride ions are negative) and hydrogen gas at the negative electrode (hydrogen ions are positive). A solution of sodium hydroxide is also formed.

There are uses for these products.

- Chlorine is used to kill bacteria in drinking water and in swimming pools.
- Chlorine is used in the manufacture of disinfectants, bleaches and in the plastic polymer PVC (polyvinyl chloride).
- Hydrogen is used in the manufacture of ammonia (the Haber process) and margarine.
- Sodium hydroxide is used in the manufacture of soap, paper and ceramics.

What happens during electrolysis?

In the electrolysis of molten sodium chloride, Cl^- ions arrive at the positive electrode. Each chloride ion loses an electron. This makes it electrically neutral – a chlorine atom again:

$$Cl^- - e^- \rightarrow Cl$$

However, you need two atoms to make chlorine gas so:

$$2Cl^- - 2e^- \rightarrow Cl_2$$

Help

A simple test for chlorine gas is that it bleaches damp litmus paper.

More uses for the halides

Silver chloride, bromide and iodide (the silver halides) are reduced to silver by the action of light, X-rays and radiation. They are used to make photographic film and photographic paper.

Hydrogen halides (e.g. hydrogen chloride) are gases which dissolve in water to produce acidic solutions.

Questions

1 The electrolysis of aqueous sodium chloride produces a number of useful substances. Draw a spider diagram which shows the substances and their uses in industry. Useful substances from the electrolysis of aqueous sodium chloride should be at the centre of the diagram.

2 What happens at the positive electrode during the electrolysis of molten sodium chloride?

3 Why are the halogens so reactive?

4 Give *one* example of a displacement reaction involving the halogens.

Forming compounds

Redox reactions

Positively charged ions gain electrons at the negatively charged electrode (**reduction**). At the positive electrode, negatively charged ions lose electrons (**oxidation**).

In a chemical reaction, if oxidation occurs then reduction must also occur – because if one ion is losing an electron then another ion must be gaining one. These are called **redox reactions**.

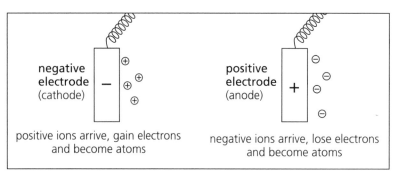

What happens in a redox reaction during electrolysis

Neutralisation

An acid and an alkali react together to produce a salt plus water – this is a **neutralisation** reaction:

acid + alkali → salt + water

The salt produced depends on:

- the metal in the alkali
- the acid used.

Neutralising hydrochloric acid produces chlorides:

hydrochloric acid + sodium hydroxide → sodium chloride + water
$$HCl + NaOH \rightarrow NaCl + H_2O$$

Neutralising nitric acid produces nitrates:

nitric acid + sodium hydroxide → sodium nitrate + water
$$HNO_3 + NaOH \rightarrow NaNO_3 + H_2O$$

Neutralising sulphuric acid produces sulphates:

sulphuric acid + sodium hydroxide → sodium sulphate + water
$$H_2SO_4 + 2NaOH \rightarrow Na_2SO_4 + 2H_2O$$

Help

Sodium chloride is a salt. It is also called salt. There are many other 'salts' (e.g. potassium nitrate, calcium sulphate). So salt is not the only salt!

Measuring pH

A solution may be neutral, acidic or alkaline. Water is neutral. Indicators show the pH of a liquid.

The pH scale is:

0	7	14

$\longleftarrow$ increasing acidity   neutral   increasing alkalinity $\longrightarrow$

Properties of compounds

Some metal and non-metal compounds dissolve in water.

Soluble oxides of non-metals (e.g. carbon dioxide, sulphur dioxide and nitrogen dioxide) produce acidic solutions. For example:

carbon dioxide + water → carbonic acid
$$CO_2 + H_2O \rightarrow H_2CO_3$$

Some metal oxides and hydroxides (e.g. the oxides and hydroxides of sodium, potassium and, to some extent calcium) dissolve in water to produce alkaline solutions. For example:

potassium + water → hydrogen + potassium hydroxide
$$2K + 2H_2O \rightarrow H_2 + 2KOH$$

The potassium hydroxide dissolves in the water to produce an alkaline solution.

Questions

1 What is a redox reaction?

2 What is meant by a neutralisation reaction?

3 Predict the salts that will result from these neutralisation reactions. Copy and complete the table.

+	hydrochloric acid	sulphuric acid
potassium hydroxide		
calcium hydroxide		

4 Write down the chemical reaction between KOH and HCl.

5 Predict the reaction between sulphur dioxide and water and write down the chemical equation.

Important symbols about chemicals

You should be able to recognise and explain what these symbols mean:

 oxidising
provide oxygen which
allows other materials
to burn more fiercely

 harmful
similar to toxic
substances but less
dangerous

 toxic
can cause death when
swallowed or breathed
in or absorbed
through the skin

 highly flammable
catch fire easily

 corrosive
attack and destroy
living tissues,
including
eyes and skin

 irritant
not corrosive but
can cause
reddening or
blistering of the skin

You should also be able to name one hazardous substance which is corrosive (e.g. sulphuric acid).

Rates of reaction

If you want to increase the speed of a reaction then you could:

- increase the **temperature** – to increase the speed and frequency at which the particles in the reacting chemicals bump into each other

heat

- increase the **concentration** of the reacting chemicals – so that particles bump into each other more often

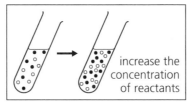
increase the concentration of reactants

- increase the **pressure** on the reacting chemicals (if gases) – to increase the rate and frequency at which particles bump into each other

if a gas you can increase the pressure

- increase the **surface area** of the chemicals (e.g. chop up a solid) – this also increases how often the particles bump into each other

increase the surface area

- use a **catalyst** – this lowers the amount of energy needed for a reaction to take place.

add a catalyst

Speeding up rate of reaction

How can you tell if a reaction has speeded up?

There are two ways:

- measure the rate products are formed (e.g. how much gas is being given off)
- measure the rate at which the chemicals disappear (e.g. a solid will get smaller).

It is possible, therefore, to compare rates of reaction. For example, when marble chips react with acid, hydrogen gas is given off and the solid chips get smaller. You can measure this.

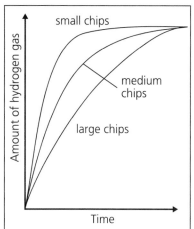

Comparing rates of reaction when marble chips are added to acid

Why speed up a reaction?

In industry, speeding up a reaction will keep costs down and therefore profits up. You will make more of your product in the same time.

Many industrial processes use catalysts. A catalyst will speed up the reaction but it is not used up itself. It can be used time and time again. Different reactions need different catalysts.

Questions

1 Suggest *three* ways of speeding up a chemical reaction. For each way explain why the reaction does speed up.

2 What are catalysts and why do industrial companies use them?

3 Suggest why industry might want to speed up reactions.

Do chemical reactions release energy?

The answer is sometimes!

An **exothermic** reaction results in energy being transferred *to* the surroundings, often in the form of heat (e.g. a fuel burning).
An **endothermic** reaction results in energy being taken *from* the surroundings.

During a chemical reaction:

• energy must be supplied to break the existing bonds between the chemicals

• energy is then released when new chemical bonds form.

In an **exothermic** reaction the energy released in forming the new bonds is *greater* than the energy used to break the original bonds – the excess energy is lost as heat. In an **endothermic** reaction the energy released in forming the new bonds is *less* than the energy used to break the original bonds – energy is therefore taken from the surroundings.

 Worked example

Q   Is the combustion of methane an exothermic or endothermic reaction?

A   The equation for the reaction is:

    methane + oxygen → carbon dioxide + water
      CH_4 + $2O_2$ → CO_2 + $2H_2O$

The energy needed to make or break bonds has been worked out and can be used to answer this question.

These are the bonds represented in this reaction:
• methane has 4 C–H bonds
• each oxygen has 1 O=O bond
• carbon dioxide has 2 C=O bonds
• each water has 2 H–O bonds.

The energy needed to make or break each of these bonds is shown in the table.

Bonds broken:
   4 C–H × 413 = 1652 kJ
   2 O=O × 498 = 996 kJ
   (two molecules of oxygen)
   Total = 2648 kJ energy used

Bonds made:
   2 C=O × 805 = 1610 kJ
   4 H–O × 464 = 1856 kJ
   (two molecules of water)
   Total = 3466 kJ energy released

Bond	Energy
C–H	413 kJ
O=O	498 kJ
C=O	805 kJ
H–O	464 kJ

More energy is released than used, so the reaction is exothermic.

 Help

kJ = kilojoule
which is 1000 joules

 Help

Remember: energy is used to break bonds and energy is released when bonds are formed.

The difference between the energy used and the energy released is known as the **nett energy transfer**. If the reaction is exothermic this is negative, if it is endothermic it is positive.

The nett energy for the worked example is:

energy in	2150 kJ
energy out	3466 kJ
nett energy gain	−1316 kJ

A chemical reaction will take place only if the particles hit each other (collide) with enough energy. The minimum energy that is needed for a reaction to take place is called the **activation energy.**

The energy changes during a reaction can be shown by graphs.

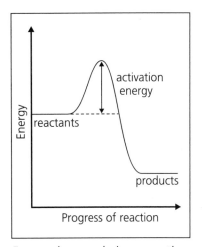

Energy changes during a reaction

Energy changes with a catalyst

Catalysts reduce the amount of energy required to start a reaction. They therefore reduce the activation energy.

Questions

1   What is meant by an exothermic reaction?

2   Study the graph.

What does the graph tell you about the reaction between nitrogen and oxygen?

3   In a reaction more energy is used in breaking the original bonds than is released in making the new bonds. Is the reaction exothermic or endothermic?

Chemistry and living organisms

Chemical reactions do not just take place in big industrial areas.
They are taking place inside our bodies all the time. Our cells use
chemicals to release energy from food and to make new materials.
We also use some micro-organisms to make useful substances for us.
For example, **yeast** cells convert:

sugar → carbon dioxide + alcohol

This is known as **fermentation** and it is used to produce:

- alcohol for wine and beer making
- carbon dioxide – the bubbles make bread rise.

Bacteria are used to make yoghurt from milk. They convert lactose
sugar in the milk to lactic acid.

These reactions are faster when it is warm but *not* hot. Living
organisms use catalysts called **enzymes**. These are proteins and are
damaged by temperatures above about 45°C.

 Help

A simple test for carbon dioxide
is that it turns lime water milky.

The chemistry of fertiliser production

Nitrogen-based fertilisers help us to grow food. They replace the
nitrogen taken from the soil by growing plants. This means that
farmers can grow more – increase the yield of their crops. One
problem with fertiliser is that it can run off the land and into
ponds, rivers and lakes. This can contaminate our drinking water.

Ammonium nitrate fertiliser is made in the following way:

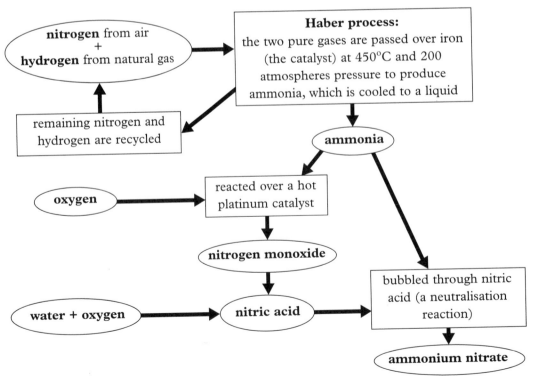

Reversible reactions and equilibrium

The reaction between nitrogen and hydrogen to produce ammonia is **reversible**. The reaction will go either way depending on the conditions.

$$N_2 + 3H_2 \xrightarrow{\text{reversible reaction}} 2NH_3$$

If the reaction is going in both directions at the same rate in a **closed system**, it is said to be in **equilibrium**. A closed system is a container where no other chemicals are involved, and where none of the products are removed from the container.

Where the point of equilibrium is between the two reactions depends on the conditions. If the forward reaction is exothermic, the back reaction must be endothermic. If you add heat energy by heating the reactants, the system will shift the reaction in favour of the back reaction which then absorbs the heat energy (you will get more reactants than products).

$$N_2 + 3H_2 \xrightarrow{\text{heat}} 2NH_3$$

So whether there are more reactant molecules or more product molecules in the equilibrium 'mix' depends on temperature. This is an important principle behind the Haber process.

The Haber process

The reaction between nitrogen and hydrogen in a closed system means that you could be breaking down ammonia as quickly as you were making it! This would be useless to a manufacturer.

A German scientist called Haber found that a high temperature, high pressure and a catalyst are needed to make even modest amounts of ammonia. The yield is increased if ammonia is siphoned off as it is made, and the unused reactants continually recycled so that it becomes an open system.

This graph shows the yields of ammonia in the Haber process at various temperatures and pressures. If pressures above 200 atmospheres are used the costs for equipment would increase significantly. If the reaction was allowed to run at lower temperature it would take too long. The temperature and pressure used are the most economic way to produce ammonia.

The reaction between nitrogen and hydrogen in different conditions

Questions

1 Micro-organisms can be used usefully by people. Draw a spider diagram to show these uses. Useful micro-organisms should be at the centre of the diagram.

2 What is meant by a reversible reaction?

3 To get the maximum yield of ammonia from nitrogen and hydrogen you would need to run the reaction at 350°C and 400 atmospheres pressure. Why do manufacturers using the Haber process not do this?

Chemical quantities

This topic is very much assessed in terms of calculations. You will, in the examination, have access to a data book. Here the information you need is printed in the table on the right.

A series of worked examples show the type of calculation you will be expected to do.

Relative formula mass of compounds

You must be able to calculate the **relative formula mass (M_r)** of a compound (given the formula).

 Worked example

Q What is the relative formula mass of sulphuric acid (H_2SO_4)?

A A_r hydrogen = 2 (there are two of them)
         A_r sulphur = 32
         A_r oxygen = 64 (there are four of them)
              $M_r = 98$

Relative atomic masses (A_r)	
hydrogen	1
carbon	12
oxygen	16
sulphur	32
calcium	40
iron	56

Percentage of elements in compounds

You must be able to work out the percentage of an element in a compound.

 Worked example

Q What is the percentage of sulphur in sulphuric acid?

A The M_r of sulphuric acid is 98
The A_r of sulphur is 32

Therefore sulphur represents $\frac{32}{98}$ of the compound

This is 32.7%

 Help

A_r is relative atomic mass.
M_r is relative formula mass.

Masses of reactants and products

You must be able to calculate the masses of reactants and products.

 Worked example

On heating calcium carbonate ($CaCO_3$) it breaks down. The products of the breakdown are calcium oxide and carbon dioxide.

Q What mass of calcium oxide can be formed from 25 g of calcium carbonate?

$$CaCO_3 \rightarrow CaO + CO_2$$

continued ...

A From this equation:

- 1 mole of $CaCO_3$ reacts to give 1 mole of CaO and 1 mole of CO_2

M_r calcium carbonate is 100   (Ca = 40, C = 12, 3 × O = 48)
M_r calcium oxide is 56   (Ca = 40, O = 16)
M_r carbon dioxide is 44   (C = 12, 2 × O = 32)

- Therefore 100 g of calcium carbonate will result in 56 g of calcium oxide.

- Therefore 25 g of calcium carbonate will result in 14 g of calcium oxide.

What if the product is a gas?

You must be able to calculate the volume of a reactant if it is a gas.

From the last example, the breakdown of 1 mole of calcium carbonate will result in 1 mole of carbon dioxide. Therefore 100 g of calcium carbonate will break down to produce 44 g of carbon dioxide.

However, 1 mole of *any* gas occupies 24 litres (at room temperature and pressure). So if 1 mole of calcium carbonate breaks down, then 24 litres of carbon dioxide are produced.

If 2 moles of calcium carbonate break down, then 2 moles of carbon dioxide will be produced, or 2 × 24 = 48 litres.

Help

Carrying out calculations involving moles is simply a matter of ratios.

Help

1 mole is the relative formula mass of the compound in grams.

Working out chemical formulae

You must be able to determine the ratios of atoms in compounds from information you are given.

 Worked example

In an investigation it is found that 5.6 g of iron react with 2.4 g of oxygen.

Q What is the formula of iron oxide?

A	**iron**	**oxygen**
masses combining	5.6 g	2.4 g
mass of 1 mole	56 g	16 g
number of moles combining	$\frac{5.6}{56} = 0.1$	$\frac{2.4}{16} = 0.15$
the ratios are	1 to	1.5
or better still	2 to	3

The formula for iron oxide is therefore Fe_2O_3.

 Questions

Use information on these pages to answer the questions.

1   What is the M_r of sulphuric acid (H_2SO_4)?

2   What is the percentage of oxygen in calcium carbonate ($CaCO_3$)?

Balancing equations

You must also be able to balance an equation given to you.

This is the reaction between sodium and chlorine.

Na + Cl$_2$ → NaCl

However, there needs to be the same number of atoms of each element on each side of the equation. So this equation becomes:

2Na + Cl$_2$ → 2NaCl

This is the reaction of methane and oxygen:

CH$_4$ + O$_2$ → H$_2$O + CO$_2$

However, there needs to be the same number of atoms of each element on each side of the equation. So this equation becomes:

CH$_4$ + 2O$_2$ → 2H$_2$O + CO$_2$

Help

Balancing equations
You must have the same number of atoms on each side of the equation.

Balancing half equations

If molten sodium chloride is electrolysed then chloride ions will move to the positive electrode. This is the equation for what happens at the positive electrode.

Cl$^-$ – e$^-$ → Cl$_2$ (a molecule of chlorine)

However, the equation doesn't balance because one molecule of chlorine contains two atoms.

You balance the equation like this:

2Cl$^-$ – 2e$^-$ → Cl$_2$

In the purification of copper, positive copper ions move to the negative electrode and are deposited as copper atoms. This is the equation for what happens at the negative electrode:

Cu^{2+} + e$^-$ → Cu

However, you must balance the equation like this:

Cu^{2+} + 2e$^-$ → Cu

Questions

1   Balance this equation which represents the breakdown of hydrogen peroxide:
    H$_2$O$_2$ → H$_2$O + O$_2$

2   34 g of ammonia react with an excess of water. How much ammonium hydroxide will be formed?
    NH$_3$ + H$_2$O → NH$_4$OH
    (nitrogen = 14, hydrogen = 1, oxygen = 16)

3   48 g of magnesium react with an excess of nitric acid. What volume of hydrogen will evolve?
    Mg + 2HNO$_3$ → Mg(NO$_3$)$_2$ + H$_2$
    (magnesium = 24, hydrogen = 1)

Exam questions

1 The table shows some of the reactions of five metals, **A, B, C, D**, and **E**. (These letters are **not** their chemical symbols.)

Metal oxide	Reaction with water	Reaction with dilute acid	Reaction with heated iron oxide
A	no reaction	moderate reaction	violent reaction
B	no reaction	slow reaction	no reaction
C	no reaction	no reaction	no reaction
D	slow reaction	fast reaction	violent reaction
E	no reaction	moderate reaction	no reaction

Use the information in the table to put the metals into their order of reactivity, from the most reactive to the least reactive. [2]

[Total 2]

2 The diagram below shows the process used to make aluminium chloride.

a Write a word equation for the reaction by which aluminium chloride is made. [1]

b Copy the two boxes below. Show how the atoms of aluminium might be arranged in the solid and the liquid. Use circles like the one already drawn to represent the aluminium atoms. [2]

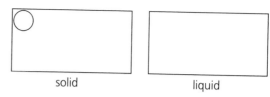

solid   liquid

c A large amount of energy is needed to turn solid aluminium into a liquid. Explain why energy is needed to turn a solid into a liquid. Your answer should make reference to the movement of the aluminium atoms. [3]

d The reaction between aluminium and chlorine is exothermic. What does 'exothermic' mean? [1]

e What is the job of the condenser in this process? [1]

[Total 8]

3 Crude oil is a complex mixture of hydrocarbons. The number of carbon atoms in the molecules ranges from 1 to over 100.

a How does the boiling point change as the number of carbon atoms in the molecules increases? [1]

b Name the method used to separate petroleum into fractions. [1]

c The simplest hydrocarbon is methane, CH_4. Its structure can be represented like this:

Draw the structure of ethane, C_2H_6. [1]

d Large hydrocarbon molecules are less useful as fuels. They can be broken down to give smaller molecules. Some of these smaller molecules are unsaturated. The simplest of these is ethene, C_2H_4.

i Name the process used to break down large hydrocarbon molecules. [1]

ii Draw the structure of ethene, C_2H_4. [1]

iii Why is ethene said to be 'unsaturated'? [1]

iv Poly(ethene) can be made from ethene. What type of substance is poly(ethene)? [1]

[Total 7]

4 a In an industrial process, electricity is passed through a solution of sodium chloride in water. A student set up the apparatus shown below to investigate this process.

i Name gas **X**.   [1]

ii Complete the half equation for the production of chlorine gas during the electrolysis:

$$—Cl^- \rightarrow —e^- + Cl_2$$ [1]

iii The student found that the solution left in the cell was alkaline. Which ion makes the solution alkaline?   [1]

b Sodium carbonate is another useful chemical that can be made from sodium chloride. The flow chart below shows one way in which sodium carbonate can be made.

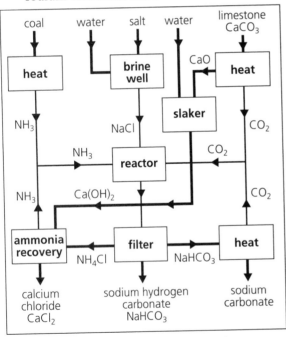

i Salt is one raw material used in this process. Name **one** other raw material used in this process.   [1]

ii Sodium carbonate is one of the products of this process. Name **one** other product.   [1]
[Total 5]

5 Diesel oil is obtained from crude oil. It can be used as a fuel for car engines. The diagram below represents a compound found in diesel oil.

H-C-C-C-C-C-C-C-C-C-C-C-C-C-C-C-C-H (with H above and below each C)

a What is the formula of this compound?   [1]

b Each of the lines on the diagram above represents a covalent bond. What is a 'covalent bond'?   [2]

c i Name the **two** products formed when pentane (C_5H_{12}) undergoes complete combustion.   [2]

ii The equation below shows the combustion of pentane. Balance the equation.

$$C_5H_{12} + —O_2 \rightarrow —CO_2 + —H_2O$$ [2]
[Total 7]

6 The bar chart shows the composition of the Earth's atmosphere today, and as it was billions of years ago.

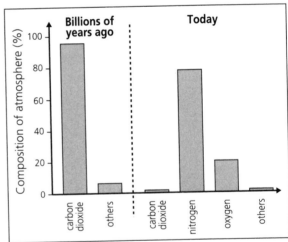

a Use information from the bar chart to describe how the atmosphere today is different from the atmosphere of billions of years ago.   [2]

b Describe the processes that have brought about the changes in the proportions of these gases in the air over billions of years.   [4]
[Total 6]

7   Earthquakes commonly occur where metamorphic rocks are being formed. The energy released in an earthquake travels as shock waves. P and S waves travel through the interior of the Earth. The diagram below shows a recording of shock waves at two different stations from a recent earthquake in Turkey.

a i How much earlier does the first P wave arrive than the first S wave at station 1?   [1]

ii What is the reason for this time difference? [1]

b Analysis of the shock wave records such as these suggests that the Earth has a layered structure. Name and briefly describe the nature of the layers.   [6]

[Total 8]

8   Propane is a gas used as a fuel in camping stoves. The equation that represents the complete combustion of propane C_3H_8 is:

$$C_3H_8 + 5O_2 \rightarrow 3CO_2 + 4H_2O$$

a Use the information below to calculate the relative amount of energy released by the combustion of propane, C_3H_8.   [4]

Bond	C–C	C–H	C=O	O=O	H–O
Bond energy	347	413	805	498	464

b The relative amount of energy released by the combustion of ethane, C_2H_6, is 1436. The combustion of propane produces more energy than the combustion of ethane. Explain why.   [3]

[Total 7]

9   The following passage was taken from a chemistry textbook.

Germanium is a white, shiny, brittle element. It is used in the electronics industry because it is able to conduct a small amount of electricity. It is made from germanium oxide obtained from the flue dusts of zinc and lead smelters. The impure germanium oxide from the flue dusts is changed into germanium by the process outlined below.

Step 1: The germanium oxide is reacted with hydrochloric acid to make germanium tetrachloride. This is a volatile liquid in which the germanium and chlorine atoms are joined by covalent bonds.

Step 2: The germanium tetrachloride is distilled off from the mixture.

Step 3: The germanium tetrachloride is added to an excess of water to produce germanium oxide and hydrochloric acid.

Steps 1–3 are repeated several times.

Step 4: The pure germanium oxide is reduced by hydrogen to form germanium.

a Balance the equation below, which represents the reaction in step 1:

$$GeO_2 + \_\_HCl \rightarrow GeCl_4 + \_\_H_2O \quad [1]$$

b Write the word equation for the reaction in step 3.   [1]

c Suggest why steps 1–3 are repeated several times.   [1]

d The equation that represents the reaction in step 4 is shown below:

$$GeO_2 + 2H_2 \rightarrow Ge + 2H_2O$$

i Explain what is meant by the term 'reduced'.   [1]

ii Calculate the mass of the germanium (g) that could be made from 525 g of germanium oxide. (Relative atomic masses: Ge = 73; O = 16.)   [3]

e Germanium is difficult to classify as either a metal or a non-metal.

i Give as much evidence as you can from the information in this question to support the view that germanium is a metal. Explain your answer as fully as you can.   [3]

ii Give as much evidence as you can from the information in this question to support the view that germanium is a non-metal. Explain your answer as fully as you can.   [3]

[Total 13]

10 a The electronic structure of a sodium atom can be written 2,8,1. Write the electronic structure of a potassium atom the same way.

[1]

b The electronic structure of a sodium atom can also be represented as in the diagram.

sodium atom

i Draw a similar diagram for a fluorine atom (2,7).

[1]

ii Draw similar diagrams to show the electronic structure of the particles in sodium fluoride.

[3]

c Why do the elements in Group 1 of the Periodic Table have similar chemical properties?

[1]

d Explain why the reactivity of the elements in Group 1 increases down the group.

[2]

[Total 8]

11 280 000 tonnes of magnesium are produced in the world each year. The pie chart below shows the ways in which magnesium is used.

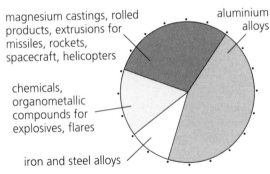

magnesium castings, rolled products, extrusions for missiles, rockets, spacecraft, helicopters

aluminium alloys

chemicals, organometallic compounds for explosives, flares

iron and steel alloys

a i Use the pie chart to calculate the percentage of magnesium used to make aluminium alloys.

[1]

ii How many tonnes of magnesium are used to make aluminium alloys each year?

[1]

b Magnesium is produced by the electrolysis of molten magnesium chloride. The reactions that take place at the electrodes are represented by the equations below.

$$Mg^{2+} + 2e^- \rightarrow Mg$$
$$2Cl^- - 2e^- \rightarrow Cl_2$$

Calculate the mass of chlorine produced when one kilogram of magnesium is made. (Relative atomic masses: Mg = 24, Cl = 35.5.)

[3]

[Total 5]

12 Joseph Priestley discovered oxygen gas in 1774 by heating mercury oxide.

A teacher repeated the experiment and found that 2.17 g of mercury oxide decomposed on heating to produce 0.16 g of oxygen.

Calculate the formula of mercury oxide. (Show all your working.) (Relative atomic masses: Hg = 201, O = 16.)

[5]

[Total 5]

13 Calcium carbonate reacts with dilute hydrochloric acid as shown in the equation below.

$$CaCO_3(s) + 2HCl(aq) \rightarrow$$
$$CaCl_2(aq) + H_2O(l) + CO_2(g)$$

The rate at which this reaction takes place can be studied by measuring the amount of carbon dioxide gas produced.

The graphs below show the results of four experiments, 1 to 4. In each experiment the amount of calcium carbonate, the volume of acid and the concentration of the acid were kept the same, but the temperature of the acid was changed each time. The calcium carbonate was in the form of small lumps of marble.

a Apart from altering the temperature, suggest **two** ways in which the reaction of calcium carbonate and hydrochloric acid could be speeded up.

[2]

b Which graph, 1 to 4, shows the results of the experiment in which the acid had the highest temperature? Explain fully how you know. [2]

c i In experiment 2, how does the rate of reaction after 1 minute compare with the rate of reaction after 2 minutes?

[1]

ii Explain, as fully as you can, why the reaction rate changes during experiment 2.

[2]

[Total 7]

14 The Haber process is used to make ammonia (NH₃) which is an important substance.

The equation below shows the reaction in which ammonia is formed.

$$N_2(g) + 3H_2(g) \rightarrow 2NH_3(g) + \textbf{heat}$$

The graph below shows how temperature and pressure affect how much ammonia is produced in the reaction.

In the industrial process a mixture of nitrogen and hydrogen is passed over iron at a temperature of about 450 °C and 200 atmospheres pressure.

a Use the graph to find the percentage of ammonia present when the temperature and pressure are 450 °C and 200 atmospheres. [2]

b Explain why the nitrogen and hydrogen mixture is passed over iron. [2]

c Explain, as fully as you can, using the graph and your knowledge of the Haber process, why 450 °C and 200 atmospheres were chosen as the conditions for this process. [8]

[Total 12]

15 This question is about sodium chloride (common salt), which is an important chemical. Sodium chloride can be made by burning sodium in chlorine gas.

a Balance the symbol equation for the reaction of sodium with chlorine. [1]

$$\textbf{Na}(s) + \textbf{Cl}_2(g) \rightarrow \textbf{NaCl}(s)$$

b During this reaction the sodium atoms are changed into sodium ions (Na⁺) and the chlorine atoms are changed into chloride ions (Cl⁻). Explain how:

i a sodium atom changes into a sodium ion; [2]

ii a chlorine atom changes into a chloride ion. [2]

c The electrolysis of sodium chloride solution is an important industrial process. The diagrams below show two experiments set up during an investigation of the electrolysis of sodium chloride.

i What would be the reading of the ammeter in experiment 1? [1]

ii Explain your answer. [2]

d The equations below show the reactions which take place in experiment 2.
$$H_2O(l) \rightarrow H^+(aq) + OH^-(aq)$$
$$2H^+(aq) + 2e^- \rightarrow H_2(g)$$
$$2Cl^-(aq) - 2e^- \rightarrow Cl_2(g)$$

i Which substance provides hydrogen ions? [1]

ii Name the products formed at the positive and negative electrodes. [2]

iii The final solution contains Na⁺(aq) and OH⁻(aq) ions. Name the useful chemical that could be obtained from this solution. [1]

[Total 12]

16 a This label has been taken from a packet of *Andrews Antacid*.

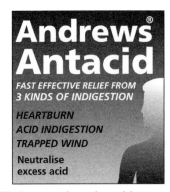

Andrews Antacid
FAST EFFECTIVE RELIEF FROM 3 KINDS OF INDIGESTION

HEARTBURN
ACID INDIGESTION
TRAPPED WIND

Neutralise excess acid

i How does the pH change when the tablets 'neutralise excess acid' in the stomach? [1]

ii Write the simplest ionic equation that represents a neutralisation reaction. [1]

iii Chewing the tablet cures indigestion faster than swallowing the tablet whole. Explain why. [1]

b The active ingredients in the *Antacid* react with hydrochloric acid in the stomach to give salts, water and carbon dioxide.

A student investigated how quickly the tablets react with excess hydrochloric acid. $40\,cm^3$ of dilute hydrochloric acid were placed in a conical flask. The flask was placed on a direct reading balance. Two *Antacid* tablets were quickly added to the flask. The apparatus was weighed immediately. At the same time, a stop clock was started. The mass was recorded every half minute for 5 minutes. The results are shown in the table.

Time (minutes)	Mass of flask + contents (g)
0.0	92.0
0.5	90.0
1.0	89.0
1.5	88.3
2.0	87.8
2.5	87.5
3.0	87.3
3.5	87.1
4.0	87.0
4.5	87.0
5.0	87.0

The main active ingredient in *Andrews Antacid* is calcium carbonate.

i Balance the equation that represents the reaction between calcium carbonate and hydrochloric acid. [1]

$$CaCO_3(s) + \underline{\quad}HCl(aq) \rightarrow CaCl_2(aq) + H_2O(l) + CO_2(g)$$

ii Why does the mass of the flask and contents decrease? [1]

c Plot the results on the graph below, and draw a smooth curve to show how the mass of the flask and its contents changes with time. Label this curve 'A'. [2]

d The student did a second experiment. The only change was that the acid was twice as concentrated. On the graph, sketch a second curve to show a possible result for this experiment. Label this curve 'B'. [2]

e Suggest **two** other ways in which the rate of reaction could be changed. [2]
[Total 11]

17 Read the following information about an element **X**.

The element **X** melts above 600 °C. It conducts electricity at room temperature. It burns in oxygen to form an oxide. When the oxide is mixed with water it turns Universal Indicator blue.

The oxide of **X** is a white solid at room temperature. It has the formula **XO** and contains the ion X^{2+}.

The element **X** reacts with chlorine to form a chloride with a high melting point. The chloride conducts electricity when molten and is soluble in water.

a From the information give **three** pieces of evidence which suggest that **X** is a metal. [3]

b In which Group of the Periodic Table should **X** be placed? Give a reason for your answer. [2]
[Total 5]
Overall total: 128 marks

AT4

Physical Processes

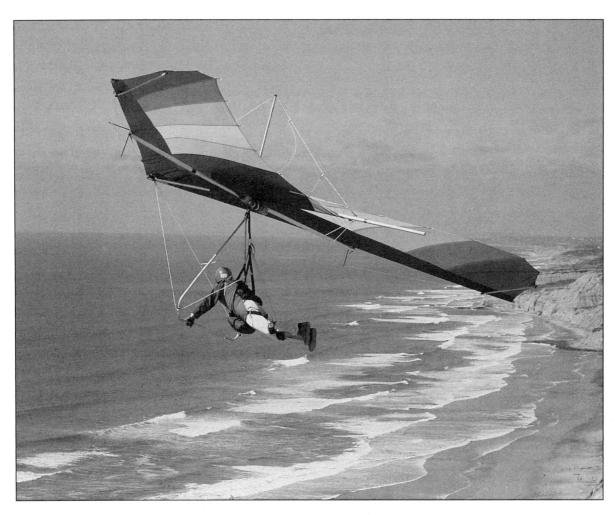

Measuring electricity

An electrical current is a flow of **charge**. It is transferring energy in the form of electricity from the mains or battery to an appliance. If this current has to pass through something which offers **resistance** (a **resistor**) the energy is converted to heat. In light bulbs this heat also provides light.

The current flowing in a circuit is measured in amperes (A) using an ammeter connected in series with the component.

Potential difference (p.d.) across a component is measured in volts (V) using a voltmeter connected across the component.

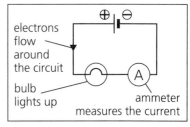

An ammeter is connected in series

The rate of energy transfer

The speed at which energy is transferred in a circuit is measured in watts (or kilowatts).

power (watts) = **potential difference** (volts) × **current** (amps)

The amount of energy transferred

How can we calculate how many joules of energy are transferred? Our equipment measures volts and amps, not joules. This formula helps us part of the way:

energy (joules) = **potential difference** (volts) × **charge** (coulombs)

A voltmeter is connected in parallel

A coulomb is the unit of charge. One coulomb equals one ampere passing through in one second, so:

charge (coulombs) = **current** (amperes) × **time** (seconds)

You can now use the reading from your ammeter to find the charge in a circuit and combine this with your readings from your voltmeter to find the amount of energy transferred.

 Worked example

Note: at the highest examination levels you have to use the results of using one formula to work out the final answer using a second formula.

Q   A current of 15 A flows through an appliance for 2 minutes. The voltage supplied to the appliance is 230 V. How much energy has been transferred?

A   energy transferred = potential difference × charge.

We only know the potential difference but we can work out the charge from:

charge = current × time
          = 15 × 120 (time is in seconds) = 1800 coulombs
energy transferred = p.d. × charge
                    = 230 × 1800 = 414 000 J

 Help

Potential difference is the difference in energy between two points in an electrical circuit. It is also called **voltage**.

Circuits

In circuits with the components connected in **series**:

- the total resistance is the sum of the resistances of the individual components
- the same current flows through each component (as the current has no alternative but to flow through all of the components)
- the total potential difference of the supply is shared between all of the components.

A series circuit with two lamps

In circuits with the components connected in **parallel**:

- there is the same potential difference (p.d.) across each component
- the current through each component depends on the resistance of the component – the greater the resistance, the smaller the current (this is because in a parallel circuit the current can flow around the circuit of least resistance)
- the total current through the whole circuit is the sum of the current running through the individual parts.

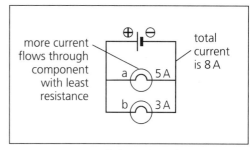

A parallel circuit with two lamps

Power supplies

The potential difference provided by each of the cells connected in series in a circuit must be added together to find the total potential difference supplied by the cells.

You must know these circuit symbols for the examination:

Help

Several *cells* connected in *series* is called a *battery*.

─o⁄o─ switch (open)	─▭─ resistor	─(A)─ ammeter
─o⁄o─ switch (closed)	─▱⁄─ variable resistor	─▱⁄─ thermistor
─┤├─ cell	─◠─ lamp	─▱─ LDR (light dependent resistor)
─┤├--┤├─ battery	─▭─ fuse	
─(▷)─ diode	─(V)─ voltmeter	

Questions

1   Power can be expressed as the amount of energy transferred in one second:

$$\text{power (watts)} = \frac{\text{energy transferred (joules)}}{\text{time (seconds)}}$$

Use this formula for finding the amount of energy transferred, to show how power can be calculated by the formula:

power (watts) = **potential difference** (volts) × **current** (amps)

2   You turn on the light switch in your bedroom. Why does the bulb give out light?

Resistance

This is the measure of how difficult it is for the current to flow. The bigger the resistance, the smaller the current produced by a particular voltage.

$$\frac{\textbf{resistance}}{\text{(ohm, } \Omega \text{)}} = \frac{\textbf{potential difference} \text{ (volts, V)}}{\textbf{current} \text{ (ampere, A)}}$$

Current–voltage graphs are used to show how the current flowing through a component varies with the voltage across the component. So the gradient of the graph shows how much resistance the component presents.

These current–voltage graphs show the effect of sending the voltage in either direction through the component:

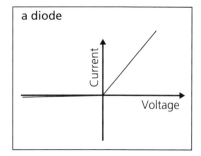

- The current through a resistor is proportional to the voltage across the resistor at the same temperatures. This means that as the voltage increases, the current increases at the same rate.

- The resistance of a filament lamp increases as the temperature of the filament increases.

- The current through a diode flows in one direction only – it has a very high resistance to current trying to flow the wrong way.

Light and temperature dependent resistors

The resistance of a light-dependent resistor decreases as the light intensity increases (e.g. a burglar alarm). The resistance of a thermistor decreases as the temperature increases (e.g a thermostat).

Static electricity

In solid conductors like copper wires the electric current is a flow of electrons. Metals are good conductors because some of the electrons from their atoms can move freely through their structure.

However, many materials which are not good conductors (i.e. through which electrons will not flow freely) can build up an electrical charge. If you take two such materials and rub them together, electrons will pass from one to the other. The materials losing electrons become positively charged. The material gaining electrons becomes negatively charged. This is **static electricity** and the materials are **electrostatically charged**.

Static electricity can be generated by rubbing strips of clear plastic and polythene on a dry woollen cloth. The polythene gains electrons and becomes negatively charged. The plastic strips lose electrons and become positively charged.

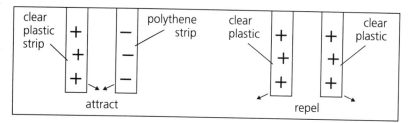

Static electricity

The greater the charge that an object picks up, the greater the potential difference (measured in volts) between the object and the Earth. If this voltage becomes large enough a spark will jump across the gap from the object to any earthed conductor. Lightning is the most dramatic example of this.

One danger: An aeroplane flying may become charged when it 'rubs' against the air as it flies. Static charges could build up in the fuelpipes, causing a spark during refuelling. However, an earth lead clamped to the metal frame of the aeroplane allows the charge to be conducted safely to Earth and prevents an explosion.

One use: A charged, fine wire mesh is present in the chimneys of coal-burning power stations. The fine particles of ash, produced by the burning of coal, have an opposite charge so 'stick' to the mesh. This prevents them going into the atmosphere.

Electrolysis

Ionic compounds are held together by electrostatic attraction. They will conduct electricity if melted or dissolved in water. Negatively charged ions (e.g. Cl^-) will move to the positive electrode. Positively charged ions (e.g. Na^+) move to the negative electrode.

The ionic compound is therefore broken down and simpler substances (products) released at the electrodes.

The amount of product released depends on:

• the size of the current

• the length of time the current is switched on.

molten sodium chloride

Questions

1   Study the current–voltage graphs on the facing page. Describe what each graph tells you about how the current varies with the voltage through the three different components.

2   Explain why you should not stand under an umbrella during a thunderstorm.

Using energy

Electrical appliances

An electrical appliance transfers energy from electricity to heat, light, sound or movement. The amount of electrical energy an appliance transfers depends on two factors:

- how long the appliance is switched on
- how fast the appliance transfers energy (this represents the power of the appliance).

Measuring power

Energy is normally measured in joules. Power is a measure of how fast this energy is transferred. The greater the power rating of an appliance, the more energy is transferred in the same time.

You do not have to remember this formula but must be able to use it:

$$\textbf{power (watt, W)} = \frac{\textbf{energy transferred (joule, J)}}{\textbf{time taken (second, s)}}$$

1 watt is therefore the transfer of 1 joule of energy in one second.

 Worked example

> **Q** A light bulb transfers 1000 J of energy in 25 seconds. What is the power rating of the appliance?
>
> **A** power = $\dfrac{\text{energy transferred}}{\text{time}}$
>
> power = $\dfrac{1000}{25}$ = 40 watts

 Help

In this worked example the unit for time is in seconds. Beware – in the examination it may be in minutes.

However, the joule is a small amount of energy compared to the amounts used at home for lighting and heating. Electricity suppliers use a much bigger unit called the **kilowatt hour**. This is based on **kilowatts** which are 1000 watts.

energy transferred = **power** × **time**
(kilowatt hour, kWh) (kilowatt, kW) (hour, h)

The amount of electrical energy transferred from the mains is measured in kilowatt hours or **units**.

 Worked example

> **Q** The power of a food mixer is rated at 20 kW and is switched on for 30 minutes. How much energy is transferred?
>
> **A** energy transfer = 20 × 0.5 (half an hour) = 10 kWh

 Help

In the examination you often have to convert units before carrying out the calculations

You can calculate the cost of energy, given the information:

cost of energy = number of units × cost per unit

Worked example

Q A house owner receives an electricity bill. The previous meter reading was 1487 units and this has risen to 1923. The cost per unit is 43.5p. How much is the cost of the electricity used?

A cost of energy = number of units × cost of each unit

$$= (1923 - 1487) \times 43.5 = £189.66$$

Electrical and heat energy are not the only forms of energy. There are other forms. One of these is **gravitational potential energy**.

Gravitational potential energy is the energy stored in an object which has been lifted against the force of gravity. The higher the object is lifted, the more energy it has.

You do not have to remember this formula but must be able to use it:

change in gravitational = weight × change in vertical height
potential energy (J)   (N)   (m)

Worked example

Q You weigh 500 N and you climb a mountain 3000 m high. What is your change in gravitational potential energy?

A change = weight × change in vertical height

$$= 500 \times 3000 = 1\,500\,000 \text{ or } 1.5 \text{ million (J)}$$

Help

The higher you climb, the more gravitational potential energy you have.

Electrical energy can be transferred as gravitational potential energy (e.g. a crane lifting a steel bar).

Worked example

Q A crane lifts a steel bar weighing 1200 N to a height of 25 m. What is the change in gravitational potential energy of the bar?

A change = weight × change in vertical height

$$= 1200 \times 25 = 30\,000 \text{ J}$$

Questions

1 A heater transfers 1500 J of energy in one minute. What is the power rating of the appliance?

2 You weigh 500 N and climb a mountain 2300 m high. What is your change in gravitational potential energy?

Heat transfer

Conduction

Substances may be hotter in one part than another part (e.g. a metal bar may be heated at one end). If energy (heat) moves through the substance from the hotter to the cooler part (without the substance itself moving) this is known as **conduction**.

Metals are good **conductors** and non-metals are usually poor conductors (**insulators**). Gases (which are non-metals) are also very poor conductors.

When a metal is heated its free electrons move more quickly. These bump into adjacent electrons and make them move more quickly as well, so energy is transferred to other parts of the metal.

Convection

Liquids and gases can flow, so they are able to **transfer** energy in the form of heat from hotter to cooler areas by their own movement. This is called **convection**.

Convection

As a liquid or gas gets hotter its particles move faster. The liquid or gas expands and becomes less dense. This means that the gas will rise, or warmer liquid will rise above surrounding cooler liquid.

Radiation

The energy transfer in **radiation** is by waves. Particles are not involved. This energy transfer can take place through space. Hot bodies (e.g. the Sun) give off mainly infrared radiation. The hotter the body, the more radiation is given off.

Dark, matt surfaces emit more radiation than shiny, white surfaces (at the same temperature). Dark, matt surfaces are also good absorbers of radiation, and shiny white surfaces are good reflectors of radiation.

 Help

Houses and cars in sunny Spain are usually white to reflect heat. People in hot countries (e.g. Saudi Arabia) often wear white clothing.

Energy loss from buildings

A lot of energy escapes from buildings in the form of heat, especially from windows and roofs. Some of the main ways in which this heat loss can be reduced include:

- double glazing – air between the two panes of glass is a very poor conductor and therefore a good insulator
- fibreglass lagging in a roof – air trapped between the fibres gives good insulation
- cavity walls – air between the bricks gives good insulation
- cavity wall insulation – air provides good insulation but if warmed it will rise and more heat lost as a result. Special foam in the cavity wall helps prevent the air rising (by convection), and so results in better insulation
- draught excluder – strips of foam around a door frame make a tight-fitting door, so warm air cannot escape.

Reducing heat loss from a house

 Questions

1. Which type of energy transfer results in heat reaching us from the Sun?

2. A radiator is turned on in a room. You are sitting at the other side of the room. You become warmer. Explain why.

3. Cavity wall insulation is expensive. Why do some houses have it, when the air in the cavity between the bricks is a good insulator anyway?

Energy efficiency

When energy is transferred from electricity some of it is usefully used and some of it is not. For example, when a radio is switched on the useful energy is the sound which you hear – however, some energy is wasted as heat.

All energy which is transferred (whether it was useful or 'wasted') eventually ends up in our surroundings, which then warm up. Once the energy has spread out like this it is very difficult to use again as it is difficult to trap.

That part of the energy which is usefully transferred gives us the efficiency of the appliance.

You do not have to remember this formula but must be able to use it:

$$\text{efficiency} = \frac{\text{useful energy transferred}}{\text{total energy supplied}}$$

 Worked example

Q A nightlight bulb has a power rating of 10 W and is switched on for 10 minutes. However, only 4500 J of the energy is used in a useful way. How efficient is this light bulb?

A energy supplied = power × time

$\qquad\qquad\quad$ = 10 × 600 (seconds)

$\qquad\qquad\quad$ = 6000 J

$\qquad$ efficiency $\qquad = \dfrac{\text{useful transfer}}{\text{total energy supplied}}$

$\qquad\qquad\qquad\quad = \dfrac{4500}{6000}$

$\qquad\qquad\qquad\quad$ = 0.75 (or 75%)

 Help

No appliances or machines are 100% efficient.

The diagrams show appliances or machines that usefully transfer energy. Each also wastes energy.

electric razor
useful transfer – movement
wasted energy – heat, noise

lamp
useful transfer – light
wasted energy – heat

computer
useful transfer – light, sound
wasted energy – some noise and heat

Energy transfers in household appliances

As you saw earlier, houses also lose energy. It is a waste of money heating a house simply for all of the heat to 'disappear' through windows, ceilings or walls. Houses are therefore insulated against this heat loss. There are various methods all shown earlier. Some cost more than others, and some are more effective that others.

Worked example

This table shows various ways to insulate one particular house against heat loss. Against each method the cost and how much it would save per year are given.

Insulation method	Cost of installing (£)	Saving per year (£)
double glazing	2000	80
draught excluders	30	40
cavity wall insulation	1000	30
extra roof insulation	300	100

Q Which method represents the best value for money in terms of reducing heat loss?

A You must work out the 'payback period' for each method. The most cost effective method will have the shortest payback time.

- The **double glazing** costs £2000 and saves £80 per year.

  It takes $\dfrac{2000}{80}$ years to pay for itself. This is **25 years**.

- The **draught excluders** cost £30 and save £40 per year.

  It takes $\dfrac{30}{40}$ years to pay for itself. This is **9 months**.

- The **cavity wall insulation** costs £1000 and saves £30 per year.

  It takes $\dfrac{1000}{30}$ years to pay for itself. This is **33.3 years**.

- The **extra roof insulation** costs £300 and saves £100 per year.

  It takes $\dfrac{300}{100}$ years to pay for itself. This is **3 years**.

Draught excluders are therefore the most cost effective in this house. The extra roof insulation saves you the most per year. The other two are expensive with long payback periods.

Questions

1 How do the following appliances usefully transfer energy?
     hair drier   toaster   television   vacuum cleaner

2 In the worked example above, suggest a reason why someone might still double glaze their house even though they know it is not cost effective.

Using electricity

Mains electricity is alternating current (a.c.). This means that the current is constantly changing direction. The frequency of change is 50 cycles per second (50 hertz or Hz).

Cells and batteries supply current flowing in one direction only – this is direct current (d.c.).

Electrical safety

Wiring plugs correctly
A correctly wired plug should look like this.

You may be given diagrams showing incorrect or unsafe wiring. You must be able to 'spot the difference'.

The **neutral** wire is earthed back at the power station. The voltage it carries, therefore, is usually close to zero.

A 3-pin plug

The **live** wire is very dangerous. Mains electricity supply is alternating (a.c.), so the live wire alternates between carrying a voltage which is sometimes positive (with respect to the neutral wire) and sometimes negative.

Fuses
Fuses protect electrical appliances. If there is a fault and an increased current flows as a result, then the fuse becomes hot and eventually breaks or 'blows'. This breaks the circuit. The fuse rating should therefore be a little higher than the current that normally flows around the circuit. If it is the same or just slightly higher than the 'normal' current then the fuse will break all of the time.

Earthing appliances
Appliances with metal covers need to be earthed. The **earth** pin in the plug is connected to the metal cover through the green/yellow wire. It is possible to get an electric shock from some appliances if this is not done.

Example: If one element of an electric fire breaks or bends and touches the metal case a large current will flow. If the fuse is blown this is reasonably safe, but if the fuse is not blown and you touch the case you might receive a fatal electric shock.

any current above 5A causes the fuse wire to break

A 5 amp fuse

Circuit breakers

Many household appliances have fuses, but circuit breakers are increasingly used instead in some appliances. They contain an electromagnet. When the current becomes high enough then the strength of the electromagnet increases sufficiently to separate a pair of contacts. This breaks the circuit. Circuit breakers work more quickly than a fuse and are easy to reset by pressing a button.

Electromagnets

If an electric current is flowing through a coil of wire it causes the coil of wire to behave like a magnet. One end of the coil becomes a North pole and the other end a South pole, like a magnet. The magnet is switched on and off, depending on whether electricity is flowing or not. So the coil is behaving as an **electromagnet**.

You can increase the strength of an electromagnet by:

- placing an iron core inside the coil
- increasing the number of turns on the coil
- increasing the size of the current flowing through the coil.

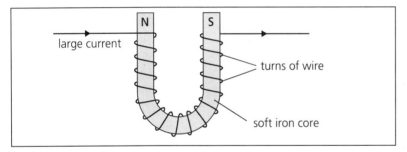

A simple electromagnet

If you reverse the current, you reverse the poles of the magnet.

If you place a wire in a magnetic field it experiences a force. The size of this force can be increased by:

- increasing the strength of the magnetic field
- increasing the size of the current flowing through the wire.

If the direction of the field or the current is reversed, the wire experiences an opposite force.

A whole range of electrical appliances and components (i.e. those with electric motors) are based on wires acting like magnets when electric currents flow through them.

Questions

1   What is meant by an alternating current?

2   Suggest *two* ways in which circuit breakers are better than fuses.

3   You make a simple electromagnet by passing a small current through a coil of wire. Give *three* ways of increasing the power of your electromagnet.

Using electromagnets in appliances

The door bell

The electromagnet in this case is used to cause a bell to ring.

This is how it works:

- You press the bell push. The circuit is complete and a current flows.
- The electromagnet works and pulls the soft iron. The hammer hits the gong.
- The contact screw is not now contacting the springy metal strip. The circuit therefore breaks and the electromagnet stops working.
- The hammer springs back. The contact screw is now in contact again with the springy metal strip, so the circuit is complete again and the current flows.
- The bell continues to ring (the hammer keeps hitting the gong) until you take your finger off the bell push and break the circuit.

Help

When you press the bell push, the circuit is continually broken and remade. So the hammer doesn't just hit the gong once, but continues to do so until you release the bell push.

The d.c. motor

An electromagnet is used to turn a coil.

This is how it works:

- The battery is turned on. The current flows. The coil turns due to the force fields from the magnets at either side.
- When the coil is vertical the forces are equal, but the momentum of the coil carries it over.
- The split ring keeps switching the direction of the current so that it flows first one way and then the other, and the coil keeps spinning.

The loudspeaker

An electromagnet is used to create sound waves.

This is how it works:

- As a current flows through the coil it develops a magnetic force.
- The magnet also has a field and the two interact.
- The cone moves (vibrates) in and out and these vibrations result in sound waves.

Relay

An electromagnet is used to help a weak current trigger a strong current.

The starter motor of a car requires 100 A to work. The current is carried in short, expensive, thick wires from the car battery. An electromagnet is used to link the switch on the dashboard, the starter motor and the battery.

This is how it works:

- The long, thin, cheap wires from the switch on the dashboard carry current which causes the electromagnet to work.
- This attracts the soft iron at the top of the pivot. The movement of the pivot closes the contacts and the circuit to the battery is complete.
- One circuit therefore results in another being 'switched on' for a short period. This is called a **relay**.

Questions

1 Explain, in your own words, how the d.c. motor works.

2 In the loudspeaker, why does the cone move in and out?

3 Why is a relay used when starting a car?

Energy sources

Electricity is very convenient but it needs to be produced.

In most power stations energy from fuel is used to heat water. The steam produced drives turbines, and these drive the generators which produce the electricity.

| fuel is burned | steam is produced | steam turns turbine | turbine drives generator | electricity is produced |

Generation of electricity

But how is the water in power stations heated?

In Britain:

- many power stations use fossil fuels (coal, oil, gas)
- some use nuclear fuel (uranium/plutonium).

Other ways of generating electricity

There are potential environmental problems associated with all the ways described above. The waste from fossil fuels can cause acid rain and global warming. The waste from nuclear reactors is difficult to dispose of safely because it is radioactive and stays so for thousands of years. Another problem is that all of the above methods rely on fuels which will run out. These are all **non-renewable energy** sources.

However, there are **renewable energy** sources which are obviously 'cleaner' for the environment. These convert other forms of energy (e.g. kinetic, electromagnetic and heat energy) into electricity. They include:

- **wind farms** – the generator is driven by the turning of the sails of many wind turbines

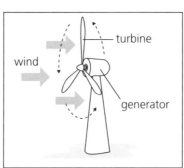

Wind power

- **tidal power** – rising and falling sea levels are used to power turbines which generate electricity

Tidal power

 Help

Non-renewable sources of energy include coal, oil, gas and nuclear sources.
Renewable sources of energy include solar, wind, tidal, hydroelectric and hot rocks.

- **hydroelectric power** – the flow of water from high points to low points can also be used to power turbines

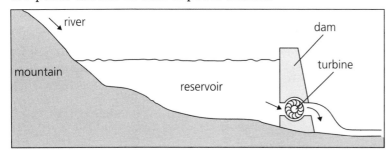

Hydroelectric power

- **solar power** – heat energy from the Sun is harnessed by solar panels to heat water; solar cells are used to convert electromagnetic energy from the Sun into electricity

Solar energy

- **steam** can also be produced by pumping water through **hot rocks** well below the surface of the Earth. The rocks are hot because at this depth below the surface radioactive elements are decaying slowly and releasing heat – just like a slow nuclear reactor.

Geothermal energy

Questions

1. Draw and complete the table to show *one* advantage and *one* disadvantage of each type of energy source.

2. Which of the sources of energy in question 1 are renewable energy sources?

3. Suggest, with reasons, suitable areas to build wind farms.

Energy source	Advantage	Disadvantage
coal		
hydroelectric		
nuclear		
wind turbine		
tidal		

Making and supplying electricity

The a.c. generator

If you rotate a coil of wire in a magnetic field (or rotate magnets around a coil of wire) then you will induce an electric current. This is how the **generator** works.

As the coil of wire cuts through the lines of force of the magnetic field, a voltage (p.d.) is produced between the ends of the wire. If the wire is part of a complete circuit then a current will flow.

Help

The generator
spinning movement within magnetic field
= electrical current

The motor
electrical current within magnetic field
= spinning movement

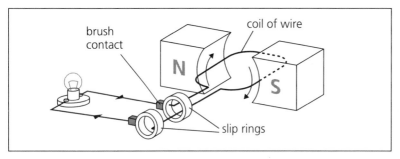

You can increase the size of the voltage by doing any, or all, of the following things:

- move the coil of wire faster
- increase the strength of the magnetic field
- increase the number of turns on the coil
- increase the area of the coil.

Why is alternating current produced?
As the coil spins, the poles will keep reversing relative to the coil. Each time they reverse, the current will flow in the opposite direction through the coil.

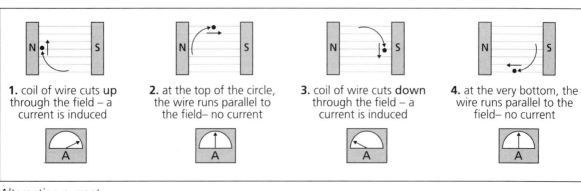

1. coil of wire cuts **up** through the field – a current is induced

2. at the top of the circle, the wire runs parallel to the field– no current

3. coil of wire cuts **down** through the field – a current is induced

4. at the very bottom, the wire runs parallel to the field– no current

Alternating current

What are the slip rings used for?
The current has to be taken away from the generator. With the coil spinning, ordinary wires would twist and break. Two continuous slip rings are used to prevent the wires twisting and to ensure that the current is a.c. (Brush contacts are used to transfer current to and from the slip rings.)

This is the principle behind electricity generating power stations. Steam is used to drive turbines which in turn drive the generators. The generators then produce electricity.

Using tidal power or hydroelectric power, it is water that drives the turbines. Steam does not need to be produced by burning fuels. These are, therefore, environmentally more 'friendly'.

Transformers

These are used at power stations to produce very high voltages for transmission through power lines. Transformers near houses then reduce this voltage so that it is useable with household appliances.

The higher the voltage transmitted in our power lines, the smaller the current needed to transmit electricity at the same rate. A high current would heat up the power lines, resulting in a waste of energy.

How does a transformer work?

A transformer consists of two separate coils wound around an iron core. When an alternating voltage is supplied to one coil (the primary coil) it induces (causes) an alternating voltage in the other coil.

The calculations are simply a matter of using ratios. The formula is:

The transformer

$$\frac{\text{voltage across primary coil}}{\text{voltage across secondary coil}} = \frac{\text{number of turns on primary coil}}{\text{number of turns on secondary coil}}$$

 Worked example

Q 200 V is supplied to the primary coil in a transformer. This coil has 50 turns. The secondary coil has 200 turns. What voltage is induced in the secondary coil?

A In terms of ratios, the secondary coil has 4 times as many turns as the primary coil. This means the induced voltage will be 4 times as great (4 × 200 V), which is 800 V.

Using the formula:

$$\frac{\text{voltage across primary}}{\text{voltage across secondary}} = \frac{\text{number of turns on primary}}{\text{number of turns on secondary}}$$

$$\frac{200}{x} = \frac{50}{200} \quad \text{or} \quad \frac{1}{4}$$

$$x = 4 \times 200 \quad \text{or} \quad 800 \text{ V}$$

 # Questions

1 A transformer is supplied with 200 V. The primary coil has 50 turns and the secondary coil has 2500 turns. What is the voltage induced?

2 You supply a transformer with 5000 V but you want to step the voltage down to 200 V. What must you make the ratio of primary to secondary turns on the coils?

Speed, velocity and acceleration

Speed

If an object moves in a straight line, the distance it has gone (from a certain point) can be shown by a distance–time graph.

The steeper the slope of the graph, the greater the speed this represents.

The speed of an object moving in a straight line and at a steady speed can be calculated using this formula:

$$\text{speed (m/s)} = \frac{\text{distance travelled (m)}}{\text{time (s)}}$$

So, for the distance–time graph shown on the right:

$$\text{speed} = \frac{40\,\text{m}}{5\,\text{s}} = 8\,\text{m/s}$$

You must be able to calculate the gradient of a distance–time graph.

 Worked example

Q A train travels 1000 m in 40 seconds. What is its speed?

A speed $= \dfrac{\text{distance}}{\text{time}}$

$= \dfrac{1000}{40} = 25\,\text{m/s}$

Help

m/s = metres per second
m = metres
s = seconds

Velocity

Velocity is the speed of an object in a straight line and in a given direction.

Velocity–time graphs represent the movement of an object travelling at a constant velocity or at a constant acceleration.

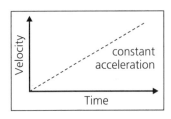

Acceleration

The acceleration of an object is the rate at which its velocity changes. For an object moving in a straight line with steady acceleration, its acceleration can be calculated by taking the change in its velocity between one point and another, and then dividing this by the time taken to get from the first point to the second.

$$\textbf{acceleration } (\text{m/s}^2) = \frac{\textbf{change in velocity } (\text{m/s})}{\textbf{time taken for the change } (\text{s})}$$

 Worked example

Q   A car accelerates from 0 to 30 m/s in 10 seconds. What is its acceleration?

A   acceleration $= \dfrac{\text{change in velocity}}{\text{time}}$

$= \dfrac{30}{10} = 3 \text{ m/s}^2$
(always remember the units)

 Help

Always remember to include units unless they are given. Examiners may use km or other units – don't be tricked!

Velocity–time graphs

You must be able to calculate:

- the gradient of a velocity–time graph (and interpret this as acceleration)

- the area under a velocity–time graph for an object moving with constant acceleration (and interpret this as distance travelled).

 Worked example

Q   An aeroplane accelerates towards take-off. The graph shows how its velocity changes in the first four seconds. What distance does it travel in this time?

A   • The area of the graph is
80 (4 × 20)

   • The area under the velocity–time line is
40 (0.5 × 4 × 20)

   • So the distance travelled is 40 m.

 Questions

1   A car travels 60 m in the first 4 seconds of its journey. Calculate its average velocity and acceleration.

2   You get on your bike to go to the local shop. You accelerate until you reach a constant speed. As you get closer to the shop you slow down, before stopping very suddenly as you press the brakes too hard. Draw a very simple graph to illustrate this.

3   How is velocity different to speed?

Speeding up and slowing down

Balanced forces

Wherever two objects interact they exert a force on each other. If the forces are equal and opposite they cancel each other out – they are **balanced forces**. This means that if the object is still to start with, it will not move.

Balanced forces

If an object is moving and the forces on it are balanced, it will carry on moving at the same speed. When a car is travelling at an unchanging speed the forces are balanced – the force from the engine is the same as the force opposing it.

Unbalanced forces

If the forces are not balanced, a stationary object will move. The forces are said to be **unbalanced.** In the example on the right, if the force exerted downwards by the person is more than the force exerted upwards by the chair, then the person will crash through the chair!

Unbalanced forces

A car starts to move because the engine exerts a greater force than the forces opposing it.

Unbalanced forces

Unbalanced forces are also needed for the car to accelerate.

A stationary object always moves in the direction of the unbalanced force, and the object moving in that direction will speed up. The greater the force, the greater the acceleration of the object. Any object moving in the opposite direction slows down. The greater the force, the more it slows down.

Downwards acceleration

Objects moving downwards are accelerated by the force of gravity. On Earth this is about 10 N/kg. Your weight is actually your mass in kilograms multiplied by the force of gravity. (This formula will be given in an examination.)

 Worked example

Q   A person on the Earth has a mass of 70 kg. What is that person's weight?

A   weight = mass × force of gravity

= 70 × 10

= 700 N (remember the units)

 Help

Weight is often wrongly expressed in kilograms – bathroom and kitchen scales show kilograms. This is actually your *mass*. Your weight should be expressed in *Newtons*.

Kinetic energy

Kinetic energy is the energy an object has because of its movement.

An object has more kinetic energy:

• the greater its mass

• the greater its speed.

kinetic energy (J) = ½ × **mass** (kg) × **speed**^{2} (m/s)

You do not have to remember this formula but must be able to use it.

 Worked example

Q   A rock has a mass of 30 kg and falls with a speed of 20 m/s. What is its kinetic energy?

A   kinetic energy = ½ mass × speed^2

= (0.5 × 30) × 20^2

= 15 × 400

= 6000 J

 Questions

1   Find out your mass in kg. Multiply this figure by 10 to work out your weight in newtons.

2   A boat is floating on the water. Describe the forces that are acting on the boat.

3   A car reverses out of a parking space. Describe the forces acting on it.

4   An aeroplane is sent to deliver relief supplies to people without food. It is unable to land because of the dangers involved. It drops a 100 kg package which falls at 30 m/s. What is the kinetic energy of the package?

Friction and work

Friction

A force of **friction** acts:

- when an object moves through air or water
- when solid surfaces slide over one another.

Friction is always opposite to the direction in which an object is travelling. It slows the object down. It also heats the object up and wears it away (e.g. an aeroplane is both slowed down and heated up due to the friction of the air). The surface of an object may 'wear away' due to friction (e.g. tyres on a car).

Brakes use friction between solid surfaces to slow cars down. The greater the speed of a car:

- the greater the braking force needed to slow the car down in the same time *or*
- the longer it takes to slow the car down, if you use the same braking force.

If you brake too hard then the car will skid as there is not enough friction between the car and the road surface.

The stopping distance of a car depends on:

- the distance the car travels during the driver's 'thinking time'
- the distance travelled while the brakes are applied.

Wet surfaces reduce friction

The stopping distance of a car increases if:

- the car is travelling faster
- the driver's reactions are slow (due to drink, drugs, tiredness)
- the road conditions are poor (wet, icy, poor visibility)
- the car is poorly maintained (worn brakes or tyres).

The faster something falls through air or a liquid, the greater the force of friction. When a body falls:

- at first it accelerates due to the force of gravity
- the force of friction eventually balances the force of gravity
- the object now falls at **terminal velocity** which is a steady speed.

force of friction

force of gravity

terminal velocity is reached when the forces are balanced

Terminal velocity

Force, mass and acceleration can all be linked in the following formula:

force (N) = **mass** (kg) × **acceleration** (m/s²)

 Worked example

Q A parachutist has a mass of 70 kg and accelerates at 8 m/s². What force is being exerted?

A force = mass × acceleration

= 70 × 8

= 560 N

 Help

You may have to rearrange any equation in an examination.

Doing 'work'

When a force moves an object then energy is transferred and work is done (e.g. you carry a bag across a room).

work done (J) = **force applied** (N) × **distance moved** (m)

 Worked example

Q Chris carried a bag of potatoes weighing 50 N for 25 m from the shop to the car. Calculate the amount of work done.

A work done = force × distance

= 50 × 25

= 1250 J

 Help

In physics, 'work done' means that energy has been transferred from one object to another.

 Questions

1 A car slows down at a rate of 6 m/s². It has a weight of 10 000 N. What force is being applied to slow the car down?

2 The same car travels 50 m. What work has been done by the engine? (Assume that there is no friction).

3 A mountaineer dislodges a stone. At first the stone accelerates down the cliff-face. After a few seconds the stone falls at a steady speed. Explain what has happened.

Pressure and stretching forces

Stretching force

If you stretch a metal wire or a spring it will return back to normal, as long as the **elastic limit** is not reached. If this limit is reached then it will remain stretched – it is permanently deformed.

Elastic potential energy is stored in the spring as it is stretched. This means that the spring is able to do work.

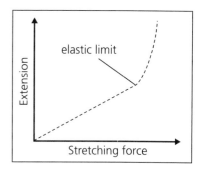

Pressure

The greater the force over an area the greater the pressure. Pressure is measured in pascals.

$$\textbf{pressure} \text{ (pascal or N/m}^2) = \frac{\textbf{force (N)}}{\textbf{area (m}^2)}$$

This applies when a force acts at right angles to an area (e.g. pushing a drawing pin into a wall).

Help

Pressure is given in N/m^2 or pascals.
1 pascal is equal to 1 N/m^2

 Worked example

This example includes a couple of 'tricks' that you should be aware of.

Q A fox is standing on the snow. It exerts a force of 100 N and each of its feet has an area of 18 cm^2. What pressure (N/m^2)does it exert on the snow?

A pressure $= \dfrac{\text{force}}{\text{area}}$

72 cm^2 = 0.0072 m^2 (the fox has four feet!)

pressure $= \dfrac{100}{0.0072}$

$= 13\,900 \text{ N/m}^2 = 13\,900 \text{ pascals}$

You must be careful in an examination to work in the correct units and to think about a question before you start. Convert the cm^2 to m^2 before you start to get your answer in the right units. This is a particularly difficult example.

Hydraulic systems

These are used as **force multipliers**. For example, if you press on the brake pedal of a car the car will stop. The force you have applied to the brake pedal is multiplied sufficiently for the car brakes to stop the car.

What is happening?
The brake pedal is pressed. The brake fluid is put under pressure. The liquid puts pressure on the slave piston which exerts pressure on the brake (see worked example on facing page).

The pressure in a liquid (or gas) acts equally in all directions, so force can be multiplied in whichever direction you require. In a liquid, pressure increases with depth.

Worked example

Q What force will be exerted on piston B?

A You must first work out the pressure that piston A exerts.

$$\text{pressure} = \frac{\text{force}}{\text{area}}$$

$$= \frac{1}{0.01}$$

$$= 100\,\text{N/m}^2$$

Now using this information, the force exerted by piston B can be worked out.

$$\text{pressure} = \frac{\text{force}}{\text{area}}$$

therefore:

force = pressure × area

= 100 × 0.5

= 50 N

force 1 N

load

liquid

master cylinder
piston A
(0.01 m²)

slave cylinder
piston B
(0.5 m²)

If you simply used ratios, then the master cylinder has an area 50 times smaller than the slave cylinder. The slave cylinder will therefore exert 50 times the force.

50 × 1 newton = 50 N.

Gases

When the pressure on a gas increases and the temperature of the gas stays the same then the volume of the gas decreases.

initial pressure × initial volume = final pressure × final volume

You may be asked to use pascals or atmospheres as units of pressure.

Worked example

Q The pressure on 500 cm³ of a gas is increased from 100 N to 200 N. What volume will it now occupy?

A initial pressure × initial volume = final pressure × final volume

On the left-hand side of the equation
100 × 500 = 50 000

On the right-hand side of the equation
50 000 divided by the pressure will give the new volume (50 000 ÷ 200).

The new volume is therefore 250 cm³.

Questions

1. A master cylinder has a surface area of 0.1m². A force of 20 N is exerted on it. The slave cylinder has an area of 0.4m². What force will the slave cylinder exert?

2. Why is it so difficult to explore the deepest parts of the oceans?

Waves

Light and sound behave like waves. When a ray of light is **reflected** from a flat, shiny surface (e.g. a plane mirror), the angle it leaves the surface is the same as the angle at which it hits the surface.

If a ray of light crosses from one transparent substance into another (e.g. from air into glass) then the ray usually changes direction – it **refracts**.

The only time it does not change direction is when it meets the boundary between the two substances at right angles, along a **normal** (that is, a line perpendicular to the boundary).

When a ray of light travels from glass, perspex or water into the air, some of the light is also reflected from the boundary.

Sound is also refracted in this way. Sound waves change direction when they cross the boundary between different substances at angles less than a right angle.

Reflection

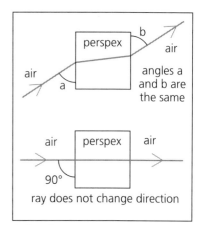

Refraction

Other types of wave

There are other sorts of waves. You can produce them in ropes and springs as well as ripples on the surface of a pond.

Waves travelling along a rope, along a spring or across water can be reflected. Waves travelling across water can also be refracted if the wave enters a deeper or a shallower area (unless their direction of travel is along the normal).

It is the change in speed of the waves of water (as they cross the boundary from deeper to shallower water) that causes the change in direction.

This behaviour shown by waves suggests that:

- light and sound also travel as waves
- light and sound waves are refracted, because they will travel at different speeds as they cross a boundary from one substance to another.

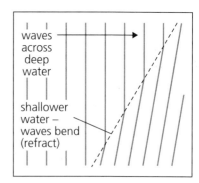

Waves refract

How waves travel

A wave is a regular pattern of disturbances, usually through a substance such as water, air, rope, a spring and so on. Only light waves are able to travel through a vacuum (that is, they do not need to be carried by any substance).

A wave moves energy from one place to another without transferring any matter. So, for example, a wave travelling through a spring does not carry the metal from the beginning to the end of the spring.

Types of wave movement

There are two types of wave movement.

Transverse waves
The disturbances in transverse waves travel at right angles to the direction that the wave is travelling. This is what you probably imagine when you think of a wave. Waves through water and rope travel this way. Light waves are also transverse waves.

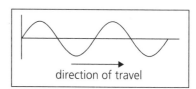
A transverse wave

Longitudinal waves
The disturbances are in the direction of travel. This is the way that waves travel through springs. It is also the way that sound waves travel through solids, liquids and gases.

A longitudinal wave

Measuring waves

You need to know three things about waves: their height, length and frequency. These can most easily be seen on a transverse wave.

- The height (maximum disturbance) of the wave is called its **amplitude.**

- The distance between a particular point on one 'peak' of the wave and the next is the **wavelength.**

- The number of waves passing a particular point each second (or produced by the source) is the **frequency.** This is measured in **hertz** (Hz).

All of these measures also apply to longitudinal waves.

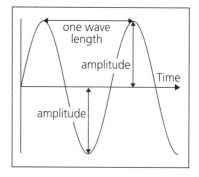

Wave speed

The speed at which a wave is travelling can be found by:

wave speed (m/s) **= frequency** (Hz) × **wavelength** (m)

 Worked example

Q A wave has a speed of 50 m/s and a frequency of 10 hertz. What is the wavelength of the wave?

A wavelength $= \dfrac{\text{wave speed}}{\text{frequency}}$

$ = \dfrac{50}{10} = 5\,\text{m}$

 Questions

1 When you stand in water up to your knees, the lower half of your legs look shorter and 'bent'. Explain this.

2 Draw a transverse wave. Mark on your diagram the amplitude and wavelength of your wave.

Using reflection and refraction

Ultrasound

A vibrating object produces a sound. The greater the amplitude (size) of the vibrations, the louder the sound.

The number of complete vibrations per second is the frequency (hertz). The higher the frequency, the higher the **pitch** of the sound.

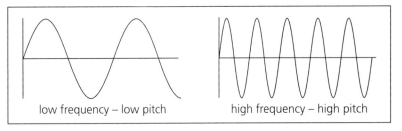

low frequency – low pitch   high frequency – high pitch

An electronic system can be used to produce electrical oscillations with any frequency, and these can be used to produce **ultrasonic waves**. Their frequency is higher than humans can hear.

Ultrasound is used:

- in industry – for cleaning and quality control (e.g. detecting flaws in metals, perhaps in bridges)

- in medicine – for pre-natal scanning (forming pictures of the baby in the womb)

- in liquids –for cleaning delicate instruments without having to take them apart.

ultrasound scanner moved over the abdomen (above the womb)

image of baby in womb

These scans work because the ultrasound waves are reflected when they meet a boundary between two different media (e.g. the growing baby and the fluid in the womb). The time taken for the reflections of ultrasonic pulses to reach a detector is a measure of how far away this boundary is. The detector is placed near to the source. Information about the time taken for reflections to travel is usually presented as a visual display of the body or the object being scanned.

Earthquakes

An earthquake produces shock waves. These are seismic waves and have been used to study the structure of the Earth. Seismographs detect the waves.

There are two types of wave:

- P waves are fast, longitudinal and travel through liquids and solids
- S waves are slower, transverse and travel only through solids.

Both types travel faster through denser materials.

- If the density of the material changes gradually then the waves travel in a curved path.
- If the density changes quickly then the direction of the waves changes abruptly.

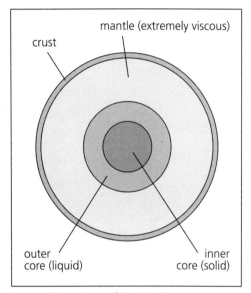

Layered structure of the Earth

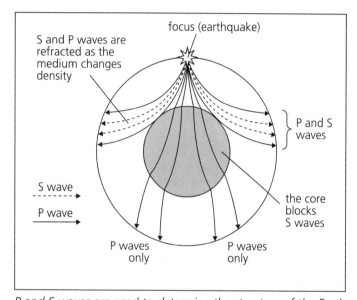

P and S waves are used to determine the structure of the Earth

If the paths of these waves are observed, then the results suggest the Earth has a layered structure with:

- a thin crust
- an extremely viscous mantle (density increasing with depth) which goes almost half way to the centre of the Earth
- a core, just over half of the Earth's diameter – outer part liquid, inner part solid.

 ## Questions

1 When engineers use ultrasonic waves to check bridges, what do you think they are checking?

2 How are both P and S waves used to determine the structure of the Earth? Explain your answer in terms of the nature of the waves and in terms of refraction.

Electromagnetic radiation

If you pass white light through a prism, the light splits into different colours because each colour is refracted to a different extent. This results in a spectrum of light which has the same colours (and in the same order) as a rainbow.

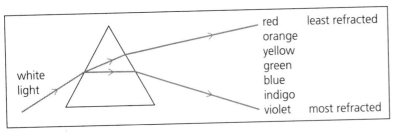

red — least refracted
orange
yellow
green
blue
indigo
violet — most refracted
white light

Help

Remember:
Richard **Of** **Y**ork **G**ained
Battles **In** **V**ain

The colours are refracted at different angles because they have different wavelengths.

Light is only one type of **electromagnetic radiation**. There are other types which you cannot see. They form a continuous spectrum. All types of electromagnetic radiation travel at the same speed (the 'speed of light') through space (a vacuum).

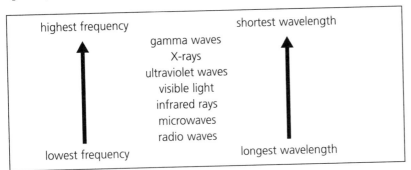

highest frequency   shortest wavelength

gamma waves
X-rays
ultraviolet waves
visible light
infrared rays
microwaves
radio waves

lowest frequency   longest wavelength

Uses of electromagnetic radiation

Different wavelengths are reflected, absorbed or transmitted in different ways, depending on the substance and the type of surface. When electromagnetic radiation is absorbed by an object or a surface:

- it makes the substance hotter
- it may create an alternating electric current with the same frequency as the radiation itself.

The uses and the effects of the different types of radiation depend on these properties as well as others.

Radio waves
Radio waves are used to transmit radio and television programmes across the Earth. The longer wavelength radio waves are reflected back down to Earth by an electrically charged layer in the upper atmosphere. It is therefore possible to send these waves long distances, despite the curvature of the Earth.

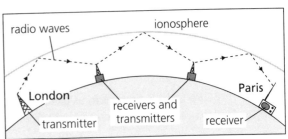

radio waves   ionosphere

London
transmitter
receivers and transmitters
Paris
receiver

Microwave radiation

Microwave radiation has wavelengths which can easily pass through the Earth's atmosphere. It is therefore used to send information to and from satellites in orbit. This type of radiation has wavelengths strongly absorbed by water molecules, so is used in microwave cooking.

source

microwaves strongly absorbed by water molecules, which vibrate more and cause the liquid or food to heat up and cook

Infrared radiation

Infrared radiation is used in grills, toasters and radiant heaters (e.g. electric fires). It is also used in optical fibre communications and for television and video remote controls.

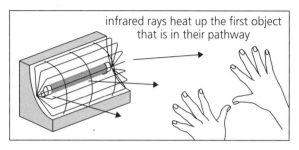

infrared rays heat up the first object that is in their pathway

Ultraviolet radiation

Some people use ultraviolet radiation to get a sun tan on a sun bed. We can all get a natural tan from the Sun's UV radiation. Special coatings, which absorb UV radiation and then emit it as light, are used in fluorescent lamps and in security coding.

UV light

X radiation

X radiation is used in X-rays. These can be 'shadow' pictures of bones or metals. These pictures can be used to identify broken bones or problems in metal structures.

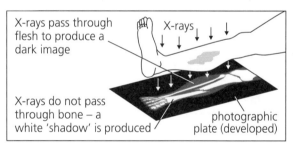

X-rays pass through flesh to produce a dark image

X-rays

X-rays do not pass through bone – a white 'shadow' is produced

photographic plate (developed)

Gamma radiation

Gamma radiation has several uses:

- to kill harmful bacteria in food and make it sterile
- to sterilise surgical instruments
- to kill cancer cells.

gamma radiation is used for sterilising medical equipment

Questions

1. List the following types of electromagnetic radiation from that with the shortest wavelength to that with the longest: UV, X-rays, microwaves and radio waves.

2. Give *two* uses of infrared radiation.

3. Suggest an explanation for how a rainbow is formed.

More uses of waves

Diffraction

When a wave moves through a gap or spreads out as it passes an obstacle, the wave spreads out from the edges. This is called **diffraction.**

Electromagnetic radiation and sound can be diffracted. This supports the idea that they travel as waves.

It is because of diffraction that:

• sounds may be heard in the shadow of buildings (around corners)

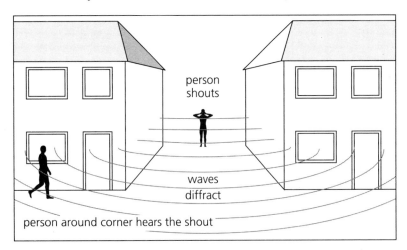

• radio signals can sometimes be picked up in the shadow of hills.

Total internal reflection

If the angle between the light ray and the normal is greater than a certain **critical angle** (different for different substances), then **total internal reflection** occurs.

This is the how optical fibres work. For example, endoscopes containing optical fibres are used by doctors to see into parts of patients' bodies such as the gut and blood vessels. Light stays in the optical fibre until it comes out of the other end.

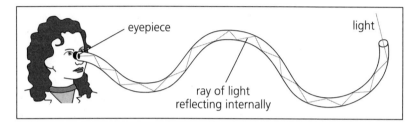

An endoscope

Another important use of total internal reflection is in communications. Optical fibres can carry more electrical signals than cables of the same diameter. The signal also weakens less on its journey than in cables.

A mirage on a hot day is another example of total internal reflection. As heat rises from the ground, the air above forms layers of different densities. Some sunlight is refracted through these layers until it reaches the critical angle when the rays totally internally reflect back up through the layers, producing an image of the sky superimposed over the normal view of the ground.

A mirage

Another use of total internal reflection involves the lighting of dials on a car dashboard, without the need for light bulbs.

Questions

1   A doctor is able to use an endoscope to see into your gut. Explain, in your own words, how this is possible.

2   You are watching the waves come through a narrow harbour entrance. You notice that the small boats inside the harbour wall are 'bobbing' up and down. Explain why they are doing this.

The effects of radiation

Electromagnetic radiation

The effect on living cells depends on the type of radiation:

- **microwaves** – the energy is absorbed by the water of living cells and may kill them
- **infrared** radiation is absorbed by the skin and we get hot
- **ultraviolet** radiation can pass through the skin to deeper tissues – the darker the skin, the more UV radiation it absorbs and the less reaches deeper tissues
- **X-rays and gamma rays** mostly pass through the soft tissues but some is absorbed by cells.

High doses of UV, X or gamma radiation can kill normal cells.

Lower doses can cause normal cells to become abnormal, which may result in cancer cells.

Radioactive substances

Some substances give out radiation all of the time. There are three types of radiation emitted by these radioactive substances:

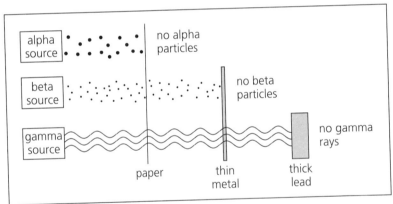

- **alpha radiation** – easily absorbed by a few centimetres of air or a thin sheet of paper
- **beta radiation** – passes through paper but will be absorbed by a few millimetres of metal
- **gamma radiation** – very penetrating and requires many centimetres of lead or several metres of concrete to stop it.

How do we explain this? The three types of radiation are all different:

- alpha (α) particles are the same as a helium nucleus – they consist of 2 protons and 2 neutrons
- beta (β) particles are very fast-moving electrons – for each beta particle emitted by a radioactive substance, one proton becomes one neutron
- gamma (γ) rays are very short wavelength electromagnetic radiation – no particles are emitted.

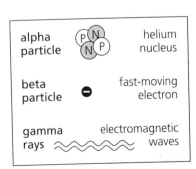

When a radioactive substance emits alpha or beta particles, its atoms change from one element to another (because the number of protons changes). For example:

- radium $^{226}_{88}Ra$ loses an alpha particle (^4_2He) and becomes radon $^{222}_{86}Rn$
- polonium $^{218}_{84}Po$ loses a beta particle ($^0_{-1}e$) and becomes astatine $^{218}_{85}At$.

There are radioactive substances all around us. They are in the ground, the air, building materials and food. We also receive radiation from space. All of this we call **background radiation**.

When radiation collides with neutral atoms or molecules then these may become **ionised** (charged). If this happens in living cells cancers may result. Alpha particles are strongly ionising. The larger the dose or radiation, the greater the risk. Even higher doses of radiation can be used to kill cancer cells or harmful micro-organisms.

The **dangers of radiation** to humans depend on where the source is:

Source outside the body	Source inside the body
beta and gamma radiation are the most dangerous as they can pass into the body and be absorbed by cells and therefore damage them	alpha radiation becomes the most dangerous as it is strongly absorbed by cells and is strongly ionising
alpha radiation is unlikely to reach the cells	beta and gamma radiation are less dangerous as they are less strongly absorbed

Using radiation

Certain substances will absorb different forms of radiation. This means that a radioactive source can be used to monitor or control the thickness of materials manufactured in industry (e.g. paper).

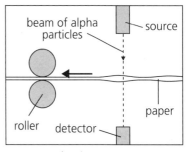

Paper production

- If the paper is too thick, not enough alpha particles will pass through to the detector so the rollers are adjusted to make the paper thinner.
- If the paper is too thin, too many alpha particles are detected so the rollers are adjusted to make the paper thicker.

Questions

1   Some people use sun beds to get a tan. What sort of radiation do sun beds emit? Describe some of the possible advantages and some disadvantages of their use.

2   Alpha radiation is used to check the thickness of paper. Why are gamma or beta radiation sources not used?

3   The following sequence shows the radioactive decay of plutonium 242 to uranium 234:
$^{242}_{94}Pu \rightarrow ^{238}_{92}U \rightarrow ^{234}_{90}Th \rightarrow ^{234}_{91}Pa \rightarrow ^{234}_{92}U$
How does uranium decay to thorium?
How does thorium decay to protactinium?

Radioactive decay

Decay is a result of changes in the nucleus of an atom.

Atoms are made up of protons and neutrons in the nucleus with electrons orbiting the nucleus.

An atom has no charge. It has the same number of protons as electrons.

The number of protons in an atom determines what element it is (e.g. carbon always has 6, sodium always has 11).

The mass number of an element equals the number of protons and neutrons in the nucleus.

	Mass	Charge
proton	1	+
neutron	1	0
electron	negligible	–

Theories of the atom

One early theory was the 'plum pudding model'. This described the atom as a positively charged sphere with negative electrons studded throughout, like raisins in a pudding.

In 1911 Ernest Rutherford carried out an experiment in which he fired alpha particles at a very thin piece of gold foil. Most of the alpha particles went straight through, but a few were scattered at wide angles by the foil. He worked out that this could only be explained if all the positive charge was concentrated in the nucleus of the atom, not throughout the atom as in the plum pudding model. He calculated the size of the nucleus from the scatter patterns and found that it was a minute part of the atom. If an atom was the size of a school hall, its nucleus would be the size of a full stop! This work led to our current view of the atom.

Isotopes

Some atoms have different numbers of neutrons. Chlorine has always got 17 protons. However some forms have 18 neutrons and some have 20 neutrons. These are **isotopes** of chlorine.

Radioactive isotopes (radionuclides)

These have atoms with unstable nuclei. When an unstable nucleus breaks down (disintegrates):

- it emits radiation
- a different atom, with a different number of protons, results.

The older the material, the less radiation it emits. It will have passed through several half-lives.

Half-life

The **half-life** of a radioactive source is the time taken for the number of radioactive atoms to half. In other words, for the substance to become half as radioactive.

 Help

Two isotopes of chlorine are $^{35}_{17}Cl$ and $^{37}_{17}Cl$.

For example, the half-life of substance X = 100 years:

- after 50 years it is half as radioactive
- after another 50 years it has lost another half of its radioactivity and is only 25% as radioactive as when it was formed.

The graph shows this.

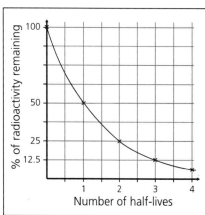

Uranium atoms have a very long half-life. They decay through a series of isotopes with short half-lives. Eventually they produce stable isotopes of lead.

If you want to date an igneous rock you can do this by working out the relative proportions of uranium and lead in the rock.

You can also use a radioisotope of potassium (potassium 40) to date rocks. It breaks down to argon. If the argon remains trapped in the igneous rock, then again you can work out the proportions and date the rock.

The nuclear process

This involves splitting atoms – a process known as **nuclear fission**.

An atom with a very large nucleus is bombarded with neutrons. This results in:

- the nucleus splitting into two smaller nuclei
- further neutrons being released – these may cause further nuclear fission and could lead to a 'chain' reaction (rods can be placed between the nuclear material to stop the chain reaction 'getting out of hand')
- new atoms being formed which are also radioactive.

The energy released during nuclear fission is very large compared to that released when a chemical bond is made between two atoms.

A nuclear chain reaction

 ## Questions

1 A substance has a half-life is 100 years. How long will it be before three quarters of its radioactivity has been lost?

2 How many protons, neutrons and electrons does uranium $^{238}_{92}U$ have?

3 The nuclear process releases a great deal of energy. How do nuclear scientists prevent a chain reaction occurring and the power station blowing up?

Moving in space

Gravity

The Earth, Sun and Moon (in fact all bodies) attract each other with a force called **gravity**. The greater the distance between bodies the smaller the force of attraction. Larger bodies have greater gravitational attraction than smaller ones.

A smaller body will stay in orbit around a larger one (e.g. the Moon around the Earth) because of the combination of its high speed and the force of attraction between the bodies. To stay in orbit at a particular distance, smaller bodies (including planets, moons and satellites) must move at a particular speed around larger bodies. The further away an orbiting body is away from the larger body, the longer it takes to make one orbit. The planets therefore move at different speeds around the Sun.

The orbits of the planets are slightly squashed circles (ellipses) with the Sun quite close to the centre.

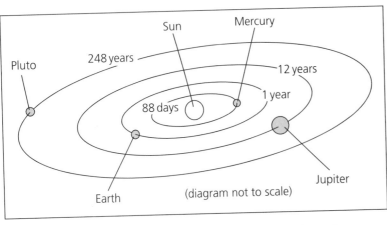

Planets orbit the Sun

(diagram not to scale)

Comets have orbits which are far from circular – sometimes they are much closer to the Sun than at other times. This is when we see them.

Satellites

Satellites are put into orbit . They have a number of uses:

- to send information between places a long way apart (e.g. TV)
- to look at weather conditions across the Earth
- to observe the Universe without the Earth's atmosphere getting in the way.

Communication satellites are usually put into orbit high above the equator and they move around the Earth at the same rate that the Earth is spinning. This means that they are always above the same place above the Earth's surface. This is known as **geostationary orbit**.

Monitoring satellites are usually put into a lower **polar orbit** above the Earth so that the Earth spins below them and they can scan whole of the Earth each day.

The origin of the Universe

Our Sun is one of many millions of stars in a group called the **Milky Way**. These stars are often many millions of times further away from us than the planets in our **solar system**.

The Universe is made up of at least a billion galaxies. **Galaxies** are often many millions of times further apart than stars within the galaxy.

The life history of a star

Stars, including the Sun, form when enough dust and gas from space is pulled together by gravitational attraction. Smaller masses also form and can be attracted by larger masses to become planets in orbit.

As stars are so massive:

- the force of gravity tends to draw the matter together
- the very high temperatures tend to make the star expand.

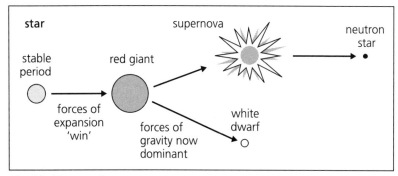

The life history of a star

During the **stable** period (which may last for billions of years) these forces are balanced. Our Sun is at this stage in its life. However, the forces of expansion then begin to 'win' and the star expands and becomes a **red giant.** It now becomes so big that the forces of expansion decrease and the force of gravity becomes the stronger force.

The star now contracts under its own gravity to become a **white dwarf** and its matter may be millions of times denser than that of Earth. If the red giant is massive enough it may rapidly contract and then explode to become a **supernova**. Dust and gas are thrown into space and a very dense **neutron star** remains.

Questions

1. State *three* uses of satellites.
2. How are satellites kept in geostationary orbit?
3. Why are monitoring satellites placed in a lower polar orbit?
4. Describe the life history of a star.

The chemistry of the stars

During a star's life the nuclei of lighter elements (mainly hydrogen and helium) gradually fuse together (nuclear fusion) to produce nuclei of a heavier element. These reactions release a lot of energy which is radiated by the stars.

Nuclei of the heaviest elements are present in the Sun and atoms of these elements are present in the inner planets of our solar system. This suggests that our solar system was formed from the material thrown out when earlier stars exploded.

The future of the Universe?

Scientists have observed that:

- light from other galaxies is shifted to the red end of the spectrum
- the further away the galaxy is, the greater this **'red shift'** becomes. This means that the wavelength of the light is becoming longer.

The current way of explaining this is that:

- other galaxies are moving away from us very quickly
- the further away a galaxy is, the faster it is moving away from us.

This suggests that the Universe is expanding and that it may have started with a huge explosion from one place. This is known as the **'big bang'** theory.

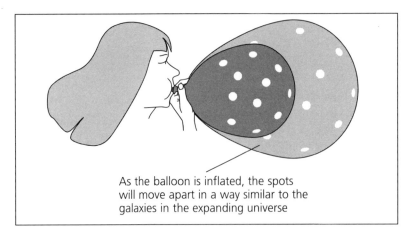

As the balloon is inflated, the spots will move apart in a way similar to the galaxies in the expanding universe

The 'big bang' theory

If the forces of expansion 'win' then the universe will continue to expand. If gravity eventually overcomes the forces of expansion, then the universe will crunch together again.

Questions

1   What evidence is there that the Universe is getting bigger?

2   What is meant by the 'red shift'?

Exam questions

1 a The diagrams show rays of light. Each ray strikes a surface of a glass block.

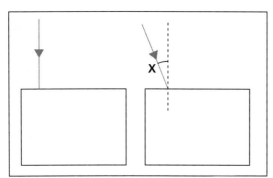

  i Copy the diagram, and draw the path of each ray through the glass block and out into the air again. [3]

  ii Mark another angle on the diagram that is equal to the angle **X**. Label this angle **Y**. [1]

b The diagrams show two beakers. Each beaker has a drawing pin inside, as shown. The first beaker is empty and the eye **cannot** see the drawing pin. The second beaker is full of water and the eye **can** see the drawing pin.

Explain how the eye is able to see the drawing pin in the second beaker. You may add to the diagram if this helps your answer. [3]

[Total 7]

2 a The diagram shows a hot water system.

  i Explain why the boiler is **below** the hot water tank. [2]

  ii Why is heat energy transferred from hot water in the tank to the surrounding air? [1]

  iii Name the process by which energy is transferred through the sides of the tank. [1]

  iv How may heat loss from the hot water tank be reduced? [2]

b One way of reducing heat loss from a house is by cavity wall insulation. Foam is pumped between the inner and outer brick walls, as shown in the diagram.

How is heat loss from a house reduced by:

  i having a cavity wall? [1]

  ii filling the cavity with foam? [1]

[Total 8]

3 Below is a distance–time graph for part of a train journey. The train is travelling at a constant speed.

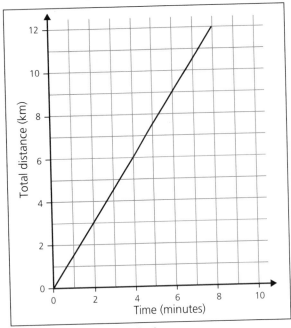

a Use the graph to find:

i how far (km) the train travels in 2 minutes; [1]

ii how long (minutes) it takes the train to travel a distance of 10 kilometres. [1]

b Calculate the speed of the train. [4]
[Total 6]

4 a A steel nail may be magnetised by an electric current. Describe, with the aid of a diagram, how you would do this. [3]

b The diagram below shows a transformer.

i Name the material used to make the core of the transformer. [1]

ii The primary coil has 48 000 turns and the secondary coil 4000 turns. If the input voltage is 240 V a.c., calculate the output voltage. [2]

iii Explain how the use of such a transformer could be adapted to transform a low voltage into a higher voltage. [1]
[Total 7]

5 Sometimes you have to change the wheel on a car. The diagram below shows the main working parts of a hydraulic car jack.

a Use your knowledge of physics to explain why using the hydraulic jack makes it easier to lift the car to change the wheel. [4]

b The diagram below shows the cylinder and pistons in more detail.

i The area of the master piston is 5 cm². An input force of 800 N is applied to this piston. Calculate the pressure exerted on the hydraulic fluid by the master piston. [3]

ii What is the pressure exerted by the hydraulic fluid on the slave piston? [1]

iii The area of the slave piston is 50 cm². Calculate the output force exerted by the slave piston. [3]
[Total 11]

6 The diagram shows apparatus used to demonstrate the motor effect. **X** is a short length of bare copper wire resting on two other wires.

a i Describe what happens to wire **X** when the current is switched on. [1]

ii What difference would you notice if the following changes were made?
A The magnetic field is reversed. [1]
B The current is increased. [1]

b The diagram shows a coil placed between the poles of a magnet. The arrows on the sides of the coil itself show the direction of the conventional current.

The arrows labelled **F** show the direction of the forces acting on the sides of the coil. Describe the motion of the coil until it comes to rest. [3]

c Most electric motors use electromagnets instead of permanent magnets. State **three** of the features of an electromagnet that control the strength of the magnetic field. [3]

[Total 9]

7 A car driver sees a dog on the road ahead and has to make an emergency stop.

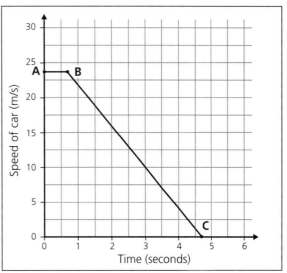

a Which part of the graph represents the 'reaction time' or 'thinking time' of the driver? [1]

b i How long is the thinking time (s) of the driver? [1]

ii Calculate the distance travelled (m) by the car during this thinking time. [2]

c Calculate the acceleration of the car after the brakes have been applied. [4]

d Calculate the distance (m) travelled by the car during braking. [3]

e The mass of the car is 800 kg. Calculate the braking force. [3]

[Total 14]

8 a A signal generator connected to a loudspeaker produces a sound wave. With the frequency of the signal generator set to 2000 Hz, the sound wave has a wavelength of 0.17 m in air. Calculate the speed of sound (m/s) in air. [3]

b The speed of sound in water is 1400 m/s. A sound wave has a frequency of 2000 Hz. Calculate its wavelength (m) in water. [3]

c Echo sounders are used at sea to locate underwater objects, such as submarines. The diagram below shows how an echo sounder works.

i What are ultrasonic waves? [1]

ii The pulse travels from the transmitter to the submarine and back to the detector. The time taken is 0.1 s. Calculate the distance (m) between the submarine and the ship. [5]

iii State **one** other use for ultrasonic waves. [1]

[Total 13]

9 Use your ideas about of waves to answer the following questions. The diagram below shows a boat anchored behind a pier. Sea waves approach the pier from the left. Despite being sheltered by the pier, the boat rocks gently up and down.

a Copy the diagram and add the waves to the right of the pier. [2]

b What is the name of the process affecting the waves as they reach the gap in the pier? [1]

[Total 3]

10 The diagram shows a diver diving from the end of a diving board.

The height of the diving board above the poolside is 4 m. The mass of the diver is 50 kg. The gravitational field strength is 10 N/kg.

a Calculate the gain in gravitational potential energy as the diver climbs from the poolside to the diving board. [4]

b The diver enters the water at a speed of 8 m/s. Calculate the kinetic energy of the diver as she hits the water. [4]

c As she hits the water, the diver's kinetic energy is not equal to the potential energy she gained as she climbed to the diving board. Explain why. [2]

[Total 10]

11 A racing driver is driving his car along a **straight** and **level** road.

a As the car's speed increases, the forward force from the engine is bigger than the backward force on the car. Eventually these forces become balanced. Explain why. [3]

b Each lap of the circuit is 4500 m. The racing car takes 90 seconds to complete one lap. Calculate the average speed of the car. [4]

c During the race the amount of fuel in the car gets less. Explain what effect this will have on the time taken to complete one lap. [3]

d The racing car has a mass of 1250 kg. It is travelling at a speed of 48 m/s. When the brake pedal is pushed down, a constant braking force of 10 000 N is exerted on the car.

i Calculate the acceleration of the car. [4]

ii The racing car travels a distance of 144 m before it stops. Calculate the work done in stopping the car. [4]

[Total 18]

12 The diagrams show a hair-dryer and the circuit inside the hair-dryer.

a Switches S_1, S_2 and S_3 are all shown in the **OFF** position. Which switch or switches have to be **ON** to make:

  i only the fan work?   [1]

  ii both heaters work?   [1]

b The following information is stamped on the hair-dryer.

> **Electrical supply 240 V 50 Hz**
>
> **Maximum power 1300 W**

During one month the hair-dryer is used for 5 hours on maximum power. Calculate:

  i the number of units of electrical energy used by the hair-dryer in that month;   [3]

  ii the cost of using the hair-dryer for 5 hours, if electrical energy costs 8p per unit.   [3]

c The plug connected to the hair-dryer has a 10 A fuse. During use a fault occurs and a surge of 25 A flows.

  i Describe and explain what happens to the fuse.   [3]

  ii How does this protect the wiring to the hair-dryer?   [2]

[Total 13]

13 The diagram below shows a musician playing an electronic keyboard. The keyboard is plugged into an amplifier to produce sound. A microphone is placed in front of the loudspeaker so that the sound can be shown as a trace on an oscilloscope.

a Explain how the sound travels from the loudspeaker to the microphone.   [3]

b The musician plays a note which has a frequency of 440 Hz. The speed of sound in air is 340 m/s. Calculate the wavelength of the resulting sound wave.   [4]

c The diagram below shows the oscilloscope trace for a note of frequency 440 Hz.

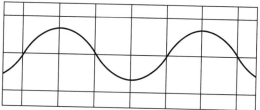

  i Draw the trace you would expect to see if the same note was played, but louder.   [2]

  ii Draw the trace you would expect to see if a note of frequency 880 Hz was played.   [2]

[Total 11]

Overall total: 130 marks

Mark scheme for AT2 exam questions

Question			Answer	Marks	Total
1	**a**		*Two of (e.g.):* • change in environment *or* habitat • new predators • new disease *or* new pathogens • new competitors for food • food source became extinct.	2	
	b		*Four of:* • decayed *or* fed on *or* digested *or* broken down *or* rotted *or* decomposed • by microbes *or* bacteria *or* fungi • by enzyme action • used for growth by microbes • eaten by detritus feeders *or* scavengers • which would respire • releasing carbon dioxide • nitrogen from proteins would be recycled.	4	**6 marks**
2	**a**		Oxygen *or* O_2. Carbon dioxide *or* CO_2.	1 1	
	b	**i**	Total water gain – total water loss = 2500 – 1000 $\qquad\qquad\qquad\qquad\qquad\qquad$ = 1500.	2	
		ii	*Three of:* • filter blood • reabsorb water • in sufficient quantities to keep body water constant • produce dilute urine if water content of body *or* blood high (*or* reverse argument) • anti-diuretic hormone • causes increased permeability • of kidney tubule.	3	**7 marks**
3	**a**	**i**	E.g. *B* and *b*.	1	
		ii	E.g. *bb* (double recessive).	1	
		iii	*Two of:* • mutation • radiation *or* X-rays • ultra-violet rays • named mutagen (e.g. mustard gas).	2	
	b		No alleles for black in the flock.	1	
	c		One bird *or* a small number of birds would be the origin of all of them so the whole flock would be likely to have only a limited variety of genes *or* alleles.	1 1	
	d		*Five of (maximum of three advantages or disadvantages):* Advantages: • identical offspring • preserve useful features • large numbers from one parent • economical *or* quick • can all be the same sex.		

		Disadvantages: • may be difficult *or* expensive to do • reduced number of alleles *or* genes in the population • cloned variety may all be susceptible to disease • ethical *or* moral reasons.		5	**12 marks**
4	**a**		*Two of (e.g.):* • wasting illness • affecting nerves *or* muscles, *or* causing twitching *or* spasms *or* clumsiness • memory loss *or* dementia *or* decline in mental activities • appears in 'middle age'.	2	
	b	**i**	50% *or* 1 in 2 *or* 1:1 (*etc.*).	1	
		ii	Sally: *Hh* Sally's husband: *hh* so chance of *H* egg being fertilised = 50%.	1 1 1	**6 marks**
5	**a**	**i**	Amount of oxygen increases. Amount of carbon dioxide decreases.	1 1	
		ii	Each heart beat pumps more blood. Heart rate increases.	1 1	
	b		*Five of:* • more oxygen to the muscles • more sugar *or* glucose to the muscles • more energy released • through respiration • more carbon dioxide removed • less lactic acid builds up • therefore less fatigue *or* tiredness shown.	5	**9 marks**
6	**a**		Trees at the lowest level; primary consumers the next level; secondary consumers at the top level. Correct shape: lowest level second largest; middle level largest; top level smallest.	1 1	
	b	**i**	$(44\,000 / 4\,600\,000) \times 100\%$ $= 0.96\%$ *(1 mark for showing working and 1 mark for answer.)*	1 1	
		ii	*Two of (e.g.):* • some heats up leaves • some is absorbed by non-photosynthetic parts • some is transmitted through leaves *or* re-radiated (not reflected) • some is lost in transpiration *or* evaporation.	2	
		iii	*Three of:* • respiration of primary consumers • movement of primary consumers • excretion *or* named waste of primary consumers • heat lost to the surroundings • death of primary consumers • not everything is eaten by primary consumers (e.g. bones).	3	
	c		Photosynthesis is limited by the temperature when cold and bright. It is limited by light at dusk *or* during the night. It is limited by carbon dioxide when the day is bright and warm.	1 1 1	

	d		*Four of*: • microbes break down the leaves • ammonium compounds are formed • these are converted to nitrates • by nitrifying bacteria (*or* correctly named bacteria) • trees can absorb the nitrates.		4	**16 marks**
7	**a**	**i**	To avoid (blood) sugar rising *or* to control blood sugar *or* to reduce the sugar level because insufficient insulin is secreted *or* produced by the body *or* because of a malfunction of the pancreas.		1 1	
		ii	Increased rate of conversion *or* more is converted from glucose *or* sugar to glycogen in the liver.		1 1 1	
		iii	*Three of*: • exercising (muscles) uses more glucose *or* sugar from the blood • this glucose *or* sugar is needed for respiration • respiration increases • this releases energy needed for exercise.		3	
	b		*Three of*: • sugar is soluble *or* has smaller molecules • it is therefore absorbed • quicker (than starch) • which has to be digested *or* sugar does not need to be digested.		3	
	c		The secretion of glucagon by the pancreas results in increased rate of conversion of glycogen into glucose *or* sugar.		1 1 1	**14 marks**
8	**a**	**i**	*One of*: • temperature • light intensity • minerals • *named* pollutant (e.g. acid rain).		1	
		ii	Higher temperature increases rate of photosynthesis *or* growth. *or* Higher light intensity increases rate of photosynthesis. *or* More minerals result in higher rate of growth. *or* (e.g.) Acid rain kills algae by (e.g.) denaturing enzymes.		1 1 1	
	b	**i**	*Four of*: • sewage provides more minerals *or* nutrients for algae *or* food for bacteria • algae grow *or* reproduce more • more food for flamingos *or* fish • increase in growth *or* reproduction of flamingos *or* fish • increase in dead algae for microbes to feed on • increase in growth *or* reproduction of microbes • increase in respiration of microbes • more oxygen is used • aquatic animals suffocate.		4	

	ii	*Three of:* • to meet the needs of an increasing population • to provide extra manufactured materials • to increase the standard of living *or* to create more jobs *or* to reduce unemployment • because industry provides more benefits than tourism.		3	**10 marks**
9 **a** **i**		Sharp reduction.		1	
	ii	Glycogen is converted to glucose which is respired to produce energy.		1 1 1	
b **i**		Athlete A's was the most effective as it resulted in the highest muscle glycogen level on the day of the race for energy release during the race.		1 1 1	
	ii	Excess carbohydrate is stored as glycogen rather than fat in the short term particularly if glycogen stores are depleted.		1 1	**9 marks**
10 **a** **i**		Increased shortly after ingestion, then dropped.		1	
	ii	Decreased shortly after ingestion, then rose.		1	
	iii	Decreased shortly after ingestion, then rose.		1	
b		*Eight of:* • ingestion of ice cools the blood flowing in the gut (wall) • the brain temperature is lowered • the reduced blood temperature is detected by the brain • impulses are sent to the sweat glands • sweat production is decreased *or* sweat pores close • evaporation of sweat is reduced • it is evaporation of sweat that cools the skin *or* the heat loss is less • therefore the skin temperature rises • because the external temperature is greater than the body temperature • *(any sensibly linked example).*		8	
c		There is natural variation in the amount of body hair in a cold environment, (having genes that produce) long hair is an advantage because hair insulates such animals are more likely to survive and pass these genes on to succeeding generations.		1 1 1 1 1	**16 marks**
11 **a**		*Four of:* • intensification is due to the need to improve the efficiency of energy transfer • it has led to the development of fast-growing crop varieties • native plants cannot compete with these • for example for light *or* water *or* minerals • herbicides have an effect • pesticides kill pollinating insects.		4	
b		Recommend a variety of measures because rotational scheme will allow these species to continue while permanent set-aside will allow others to continue leading to conservation of a wide range of species.		1 1 1 1	**8 marks**

12	a		Each 'line' of genotypes all correct: XY X and X; X and Y XX; XY	1 1 1	
	b		G 50%; H 0%. Huntington's allele is dominant. Genotype of C is hh and of D is Hh therefore G has a 50% chance of inheriting H allele. Genotypes of both E and F are hh therefore H has no chance of inheriting H allele.	1 1 1 1 1 1	**9 marks**
13	a		*Two of:* • broken down *or* digested • by enzymes *or* a named enzyme • into sugars *or* named sugar.	2	
	b		Follow diet A because it gives the highest proportion of stored sugar *or* sugar in muscles.	2	**4 marks**
14	a		glucose *or* sugar water	1 1	
	b	i	100 + 104 = 204 billion tonnes	1	
		ii	(100/204) × 100 = 49% *Incorrect answer but correct method, 1 mark.*	2	
		iii	(5 + 50 + 2 + 50 + 100) – (100 + 104) = 207 – 204 = 3 billion tonnes *Incorrect answer but correct method, 1 mark.*	2	
	c	i	*Two of:* • sulphur dioxide • nitrogen oxide • carbon monoxide.	2	
		ii	*Two of:* • soil becomes acid • freshwater becomes acid • leading to death of freshwater organisms • defoliation of trees *or* kills trees • erosion effects.	2	
	d		Bacteria *or* fungi *or* decomposers *or* microbes detritus feeders *or* named detritus feeder (e.g. earthworm) microbes feed *or* microbes break up *or* microbes decompose *or* microbes decay (reference to) respiration carbon dioxide is released	1 1 1 1 1	**16 marks**
15	a		E.g. oak trees → leaf eaters → beetles → shrews *(If no arrows or arrows point left, 1 mark only.)*	2	
	b		Small bird population would rise because fewer eaten by weasels. Moth population would fall because more would be eaten by small birds.	1 1 1 1	

				Marks	Total
c	**i**		Voles *or* small birds *or* beetles.	1	
	ii		(Oak) trees are large organisms	1	
			therefore their biomass is large	1	
			but their number is small.	1	
d	**i**		Digested *or* broken down *or* decayed *or* rotted	1	
			by microbes.	1	
	ii		March	1	
			because the temperature is higher *or* microbes *or* earthworms are more active.	1	
	iii		Microbes *or* decomposers *or* bacteria *or* fungi *or* saprophytes	1	
			break down proteins into ammonium	1	
			nitrifying bacteria *(mark for bacteria if not given as first point)*	1	
			convert ammonium to nitrate	1	
			nitrates are absorbed by plant roots	1	
			and combined with sugars to produce new protein.	1	**20 marks**

Overall total: 162 marks

Mark scheme for AT3 exam questions

Question			Answer	Marks	Total
1			**D, A, E, B, C**. *(All correct, 2 marks; if one misplaced, 1 mark.)*	2	**2 marks**
2	**a**		Aluminium + chlorine → aluminium chloride.	1	
	b		Solid: circles touching.	1	
			Liquid: circles close together, in a random arrangement, with the gaps between atoms smaller than the diameter of the atoms.	1	
	c		Energy makes the particles vibrate more:		
			the energy breaks bonds (*or* causes particles to vibrate more)	1	
			attractive forces between particles are made weaker	1	
			so the particles are more free to move around.	1	
	d		Heat *or* energy is given out.	1	
	e		To cool the aluminium chloride *or* turn it into a liquid *or* solid.	1	**8 marks**
3	**a**		The more carbon atoms, the higher the boiling point.	1	
	b		Fractional distillation.	1	
	c		H H │ │ H─C─C─H │ │ H H	1	
	d	**i**	Cracking.	1	
		ii	H─C=C─H │ │ H H	1	
		iii	It has carbon–carbon double bonds *or* it can take part in addition reactions.	1	
		iv	Polymer *or* plastic.	1	**7 marks**

4	a	i	Hydrogen.	1	
		ii	2; 2.	1	
		iii	Hydroxide *or* OH⁻.	1	
	b	i	*One of:* • coal • water • limestone.	1	
		ii	*One of:* • calcium chloride • sodium hydrogen carbonate.	1	**5 marks**
5	a		$C_{16}H_{34}$.	1	
	b		Bond made by electrons	1	
			which are shared.	1	
	c	i	Carbon dioxide.	1	
			Water.	1	
		ii	8; 5; 6. *(If only two correct, 1 mark.)*	2	**7 marks**
6	a		*Two of:* • lower amount of carbon dioxide • higher amount of oxygen • higher amount of nitrogen • lower amount of other gases *or* ammonia *or* methane.	2	
	b		*Four of:* • plants have been photosynthesising • taking in carbon dioxide • giving out oxygen • carbon dioxide from the air has been trapped in sedimentary rocks *or* fossil fuels • nitrogen has been produced by bacteria *or* living organisms *or* microbes *or* decay of dead organisms • nitrogen has been produced by reaction of ammonia with oxygen *or* by the decomposition of ammonia • water vapour has condensed • ozone has been formed from oxygen • less carbon dioxide has been released from volcanoes • nitrogen has built up because it is unreactive.	4	**6 marks**
7	a	i	45–55 seconds *or* 0.75–0.9 minutes.	1	
		ii	P waves travel faster through the Earth than S waves.	1	
	b		The crust is solid *or* rock.	1	
			The crust *or* thin layer is between 5 km and 90 km thick.	1	
			The mantle is viscous *or* molten *or* magma.	1	
			The outer core is liquid.	1	
			The inner core is solid.	1	
			The inner core is mainly iron.	1	**8 marks**
8	a		The correct bond energies are: $2 \times$ C–C = 694 $6 \times$ C=O = 4830 $8 \times$ C–H = 3304 $8 \times$ H–O = <u>3712</u> $5 \times$ O=O = <u>2490</u> 8542 Totals: 6488 *(All correct, 1 extra mark.)* Difference: 2054. *(Correct final answer only, all 4 marks.)*	1 1 1 1	

	b		Propane is larger *or* has more atoms	1	
			More bonds are broken.	1	
			More bonds are formed *or* more product is formed.	1	**7 marks**
9	**a**		4; 2.	1	
	b		Germanium tetrachloride + water → germanium oxide + hydrochloric acid.	1	
	c		To purify the germanium oxide *or* to remove impurities *or* to ensure a complete reaction *or* to increase the yield.	1	
	d	**i**	To remove oxygen *or* to add hydrogen *or* to gain electrons.	1	
		ii	$GeO_2 = 73 + (2 \times 16) = 105$	1	
			mass of germanium $= 525 \times (73/105)$	1	
			$= 365g$	1	
	e	**i**	*Three of:* • germanium is shiny *or* lustrous • it conducts a small amount of electricity • metal oxides react with acid • metal oxides are basic • metal oxides are reduced by hydrogen.	3	
		ii	*Three of:* • germanium is brittle • germanium tetrachloride is a (volatile) liquid • germanium tetrachloride is made of molecules • germanium tetrachloride has covalent bonding *or* when two non-metals react they have covalent bonding • $GeCl_4$ *or* the salt of germanium undergoes hydrolysis *or* reacts with water • germanium is not a good conductor of electricity.	3	**13 marks**
10	**a**		2,8,8,1.	1	
	b	**i**		1	
		ii	*(1 mark for the charges, 1 mark for each correct structure.)*	3	
	c		They have the same number of electrons in the outer shell *or* at the highest energy level *or* they all form 1+ ions *or* they must all lose the same number of electrons to react.	1	
	d		Electrons are lost more easily	1	
			the further they are from the nucleus *or* in a bigger atom *or* the more energy levels there are.	1	**8 marks**
11	**a**	**i**	45%	1	
		ii	$280\,000 \times 45\% = 126\,000$	1	
	b		$Cl_2 = 35.5 \times 2 = 71$	1	
			$1 \times (71/24)$	1	
			$= 2.96\,kg$	1	
			(If units not given, 3 marks. If units given but wrong, 2 marks.)		**5 marks**

12	mass of Hg = 2.17 − 0.16 = 2.01 g	1	
	moles of Hg = 2.01/201 = 0.01	1	
	moles of O = 0.16/16 = 0.01	1	
	therefore ratio = 1:1	1	
	therefore formula is HgO	1	
	(Must have working correct to get the ratio mark.)		
	or molar masses: HgO = Hg + O		
	217 = 201 + 16		
	amount of HgO = 2.17 × 100 = 217 g		
	amount of O_2 produced 0.16 × 100 = 16 g		
	therefore ratio = 1:1		
	therefore formula = HgO		**5 marks**
13 a	*Two of:*		
	• increase the concentration of acid		
	• increase the surface area of solid *or* grind up the solid		
	• add a catalyst.	2	
b	1	1	
	It is the one that makes the gas fastest (steepest curve).	1	
c i	Faster after 1 minute, slower after 2 minutes.	1	
ii	The reactants get used up	1	
	so the concentration decreases *or* there is less chance of collision.	1	**7 marks**
14 a	16%	2	
b	Iron is a catalyst	1	
	which speeds up the reaction.	1	
c	*Eight of:*		
	• (from the graph) the best yield is obtained at high pressure		
	• and low temperature		
	• it is a reversible reaction		
	• in which formation of ammonia is favoured at low temperature (the reaction is exothermic)		
	• and the formation of ammonia is favoured at high pressure, because of the greater number of gaseous reactant molecules than gaseous product molecules *or* because of the greater volume of reactant than volume of product molecules		
	• the pressure used is limited by cost *or* materials		
	• the rate of reaction is slow at low temperatures		
	• the actual temperature and pressure used is a good compromise (between a good yield and a reasonable rate)		
	• removal of the ammonia makes the rate more important than the yield.	8	**12 marks**
15 a	2Na(s) + Cl_2(g) → 2NaCl(s)	1	
b i	Sodium (atom) loses	1	
	electron.	1	
ii	Chlorine (atom) gains	1	
	electron.	1	
c i	0 amps	1	
ii	The ions	1	
	cannot move in the solid (*or* solid sodium chloride does not conduct electricity).	1	

d	**i**	Water *or* H_2O.		1	
	ii	Chlorine at the positive electrode.		1	
		Hydrogen at the negative electrode.		1	
	iii	Sodium hydroxide.		1	**12 marks**
16 a	**i**	It increases.		1	
	ii	$H^+ + OH^- \rightarrow H_2O$ (*or* $H_3O^+ + OH^- = 2H_2O$)		1	
	iii	*One of:* • smaller bits • bigger surface area • more particles open to attack by acid		1	
b	**i**	2.		1	
	ii	CO_2 *or* gas has evolved *or* gas has mass.		1	

c

Plotting points *(1 mistake allowed)*.	1
Reasonable attempt to draw the curve.	1

d	Steeper curve faster.	1
	Same final mass.	1

e *Two of:*
• stir the mixture
• change the temperature *or* heat *or* cool
• add a catalyst
• powder the tablets
• apply pressure.   2   **11 marks**

17 a *Three of:*
• high melting point *or* melts above 600 °C
• conducts (electricity)
• basic oxide *or* alkaline oxide
• chloride has high melting point
• molten chloride conducts electricity
• forms positive ions *or* forms ionic compound with non-metals
• solid at room temperature.   3

b Group 2.   1
Formula of oxide is XO *or* ion is X^{2+} *or* oxide forms alkaline solution.   1   **5 marks**

Overall total: 128 marks

Mark scheme for AT4 exam questions

Question			Answer	Marks	Total
1	a				
		i	The path for the left block is straight.	1	
			The path for the right block is bent through the block.	1	
			The path for the right block emerges at the original angle.	1	
		ii	Angle **Y**.	1	
	b				
			The light path is straight from the drawing pin (as before)	1	
			but is bent or defracted at the water surface	1	
			and then continues towards the eye.	1	**7 marks**
2	a	i	Hot water (*not* heat) rises	1	
			due to convection currents.	1	
			or Water expands *or* becomes less dense on heating		
			less dense water rises.		
		ii	The inside is hotter than the outside.	1	
		iii	Conduction.	1	
		iv	Surround *or* cover *or* insulate the tank	1	
			with a poor conductor *or* a named insulator, e.g. lagging.	1	
	b	i	Air between the bricks is a good insulator.	1	
		ii	The foam traps the air, so it cannot convect even if it warms slightly.	1	**8 marks**
3	a	i	3 km (between 2.9 km and 3.1 km allowed).	1	
		ii	6.6 minutes (between 6.5 minutes and 6.8 minutes allowed).	1	
	b		Speed = distance divided by time	1	
			= 12 divided by 8	1	
			= 1.5	1	
			km/minute	1	**6 marks**
4	a		Wind a coil around the nail	1	
			connect to the electricity supply	1	
			to pass a d.c. current.	1	
	b	i	Iron.	1	
		ii	48 000/4000 = 240/output voltage	1	
			output voltage = 20	1	
		iii	Reverse the input and output *or* increase the number of secondary turns.	1	**7 marks**

5	a		*Four of:* • liquid is incompressible • pressure is transmitted through the liquid • the force out is greater than the effort put in • the area of the slave piston is larger • the handle is a lever which amplifies the effort.	4	

	b	i	Pressure = force/area
			      = 800/5
			      = 160 N/cm^2
				1
				1
				1	

		ii	The same as in **b i**.	1	

		iii	Force = pressure × area
			     = 160 × 50
			     = 8000 N
				1
				1
				1
					11 marks

6	a	i	It moves *or* experiences a force.	1	
		ii	A The wire moves in the opposite direction *or* the force is reversed. B The wire moves faster *or* there is a larger force (*not* it moves further).	1 1	
	b		It turns clockwise it turns anticlockwise and keeps reversing it comes to rest in a vertical position.	1 1 1	
	c		The number of turns on the coil. The size of the current. Whether there is a soft, metal core.	1 1 1	**9 marks**
7	a		AB.	1	
	b	i	0.7 s	1	

		ii	Distance = speed × time
			      = 24 × 0.7
			      = 16.8 m/s
				1
				
				1	

	c		Acceleration = change in speed/time
			      = −24/4
			      = −6
			      m/s^2
				1
				1
				1
				1	

	d		Distance = average speed × time
			      = (24/2) × 4 (the average speed while coming to a stop is
			                    12 m/s)
			      = 48 m
				1
				
				1
				1	

	e		$F = ma$ (force = mass × acceleration)
			     = 800 × −6
			     = −4800 N
				1
				1
				1
					14 marks

8	a		Speed = wavelength × frequency
			      = 0.17 × 2000
			      = 340 m/s
				1
				1
				1	

	b		Wavelength = speed/frequency
			      = 1400/2000
			      = 0.7 m
				1
				1
				1	

	c	i	Longitudinal *or* sound waves of frequency above 20 000 Hz *or* above audible range *or* of a very high frequency.	1	

	ii	Distance = speed × time *(2 marks as you must rearrange*
		speed = distance/time)
		          = 1400 × 0.1
		          = 140 m
		but this is the distance to the submarine and back
		so the distance is 140/2 or 70 m
			2
			1
			1
			
			1	

	iii	*One of:* • cleaning industry • quality control in industry • baby scans.	1	**13 marks**
9				
	a	Waves correctly diffracted (spread) around pier to boat. Wavelength still constant.	1 1	
	b	Diffraction.	1	**3 marks**

10	**a**	Gravitational potential energy = mass × gravity × height
		                              = 50 × 10 × 4
		                              = 2000
		                              J
			1
			1
			1
			1	

	b	Kinetic energy = $\frac{1}{2}$ mass × velocity^2
		          = ($\frac{1}{2}$ × 50) × 8^2
		          = 1600
		          J
			1
			1
			1
			1	

	c	*Two of:* • work is done against air resistance • the fall of the diver's centre of gravity is different from the rise in climbing the stairs • part of the potential energy is used to rotate her body • she gains potential energy on take-off (she gains height).	2	**10 marks**
11	**a**	There is a maximum forward force backward *or* friction *or* resistive force increases with speed until forward and backward forces are equal.	1 1 1	

	b	Speed = distance/time
		      = 4500/90
		      = 50
		        m/s
		(Correct answer, even without working, 4 marks.)
			1
			1
			1
			1	

	c	The time will be less because the mass reduces as fuel is used so acceleration and deceleration greater *or* easier.	1 1 1	

In the diagram, labels: **waves**, **pier**

d	**i**	$F = ma$ $10\,000 = 1250 \times a$ $a = 8$ $\quad$ m/s^2 *(Correct answer, even without working, 4 marks.)*	1 1 1 1	
	ii	$W = Fd$ $\quad = 10\,000 \times 144$ $\quad = 1\,440\,000$ $\quad$ J *(Correct answer, even without working, 4 marks.)*	1 1 1 1	**18 marks**
12 a	**i**	S_3 (*or* 3).	1	
	ii	S_1, S_2 and S_3 (*or* 1, 2, 3).	1	
b	**i**	$1300\,\text{W} = 1.3\,\text{kW}$ number of units $= 1.3 \times 5$ 6.5 units	3	
	ii	52p *or* £0.52 *or* 52 *or* 0.52 *or* 6.5×8	3	
c	**i**	It melts *or* blows (*not* explodes). The large current causes heating in the wire. The fuse gets too hot *or* reaches melting point.	1 1 1	
	ii	The circuit is broken *or* the current stops flowing preventing the wire from overheating.	1 1	**13 marks**
13 a		*Three of:* • the speaker causes adjacent air molecules *or* particles to vibrate • at the same frequency as the speaker • energy is transferred from particle to particle • as a longitudinal wave • with no net air movement.	3	
b		Speed = wavelength × frequency $340 = 440 \times$ wavelength wavelength $= 0.77$ $\quad$ m *(Correct answer, even without working, 4 marks.)*	1 1 1 1	
c	**i**	Trace showing greater amplitude but with the same frequency.	1 1	
	ii	Trace showing the frequency doubled (3 cycles). *(Frequency increased but not times two, 1 mark.)*	2	**11 marks**

Overall total: 130 marks

The author is responsible for the solutions and commentaries to these exam questions.

Answers to end of spread questions

These notes accompany the questions which are to be found at the end of each double-page spread. They are not mark schemes as these questions are not the same as those you will find in your final examination. Where candidates have common misconceptions, these are added to the notes.

Humans as organisms

Page 3

1

Enzyme	Where made	What does it do?
carbohydrase	salivary gland pancreas small intestine	digests starch to sugars
protease	stomach pancreas small intestine	digests protein to amino acids
lipase	pancreas small intestine	digests fats to fatty acids and glycerol

2   Acid conditions.
3   Increases the surface area for enzymes to work on. *Pupils frequently do not know this.*

Page 5

1   Plasma transports a great many things. Those you need to know are: carbon dioxide, digested food and urea.
2   Veins have thinner walls with less muscle and elastic tissue. They also have valves to prevent backflow of blood. *Remember there are also valves in the heart to prevent backflow of blood.*
3   There are many substances exchanged. Those you need to know are: oxygen, carbon dioxide and glucose.
4   White cells help defend the body against microbes (they ingest or eat them). Red cells transport oxygen (in the haemoglobin as oxy-haemoglobin). Platelets help form scabs over cuts.
5   The red cell passes into the ventricle then the main artery. It then passes into the capillaries which form the blood supply to an organ (e.g. the liver). It will then pass into a vein leading away from the organ. It will eventually find its way into the main vein taking blood back to the right atrium of the heart.

Page 7

1   Glucose: in blood from small intestine from food you eat. *In a later chapter you will find that some may be converted to glycogen in the liver to be stored if there is already too much sugar in the blood.*

Oxygen: absorbed into blood through alveoli, picked up by haemoglobin and transported to respiring cells in body where it is released. *This is dealt with in detail on the next spread.*

2   It is carried in capillaries away from the cells. Eventually the capillaries form veins. It is transported through the heart and on to the lungs where it diffuses through the alveoli and is breathed out.
3   There is a greater surface area for the gas to diffuse through which prevents any build up (rather like preventing a traffic jam). *You will find this idea of surface area very important in biology.*
4   Diffusion is the movement of particles from an area of higher concentration to an area of lower concentration. There is a greater concentration of oxygen in the lungs than in the blood returning from the body so oxygen diffuses into the blood. The exact opposite is true for carbon dioxide.
5   When we breathe out the ribs move down and in, the diaphragm moves up, this causes an increase in pressure on the air in the lungs – so we breathe out.

Page 9

1   When watching the television the lens was its natural shape (quite thick). This is necessary to bend light rays, which are diverging quickly, to a focus. When looking at your friend the rays of light are not diverging quickly so do not need to be bent as much. The ciliary muscles relax, ligaments attached to the lens pull on the lens, the lens becomes thinner.
2   The hot kettle is the stimulus, sensory nerve endings in the fingers are triggered, a message passes along the sensory nerve to the spinal chord. A relay nerve is triggered and this passes the message on to the correct motor nerve. This nerve takes the message to an effector – in this case a muscle which contracts pulling your hand away from the kettle.
3   The impulse is an electrical message sent through the nerves. Then chemicals are released across the synapses.

Page 11

1   You are respiring quickly to release energy. Some energy is released as heat so you need to cool down. Blood vessels near the skin's surface dilate to allow more blood to flow near the surface. The blood radiates heat. The skin looks red.
2   You have lost a lot of water in sweating. The blood contains less water – it is concentrated. The pituitary gland releases ADH. The kidney tubule walls become more permeable and reabsorb more water. The urine is therefore more concentrated.
3   Your diagram should include: lung cancer, lung disease (emphysema), heart disease and disease of blood vessels.

Page 13

1 Viruses have a protein coat surrounding a few genes. There is no cell membrane or nucleus.

2 Toxins are poisons (often produced by invading microbes). White cells produce anti-toxins to neutralise them.

3 White cells will attack the microbes. White cells may produce antibodies and antitoxins to help destroy particular microbes.

4 By having a complete skin (i.e. a skin without any cuts in it). By having the air passages covered in a sticky mucus which helps trap any microbes being breathed in. Also the stomach is acidic.

5 People in much closer contact allowing microbes to transfer from one person to another either by touch or in droplets (e.g. sneezing).

Green plants as organisms

Page 15

1 Your spider diagram should include: cell wall, chlorophyll (chloroplasts) and vacuole.

2 Too cold and less light; enzymes controlling photosynthesis only working very slowly.

3 Diffuses in from air, through stomata, then diffuses through large air spaces to all cells, it then diffuses through the cell walls.
Note: a question like this could well be worth 4 marks in an exam. Make sure you write in the necessary detail.

4 Starch for storage, cellulose for cell walls, combined with other nutrients to produce proteins for growth.

5 It would have poorly formed roots and the younger leaves would have a purple colour.

6 $$\text{carbon dioxide} + \text{water} \xrightarrow[\text{chlorophyll}]{\text{light}} \text{glucose} + \text{oxygen}$$

Page 17

1 Large surface area.

2 Movement of water from an area where there is a higher concentration of water molecules to one where the concentration is lower.

3 Your diagram should include: to help new cuttings grow roots, to help ripen fruit, and as weedkillers.

Variation, inheritance and evolution

Page 19

1 Environmental and genetic.

2 A copy of each chromosome is made so that there are now four of each type of chromosome in the cell. The cell divides twice so that each new cell has only one chromosome from each original pair.

3 Because they have exactly the same genetic make up.

4 41 chromosomes, one from each original pair.

Page 21

1 One parent is SS the other is Ss. The possible combinations of the genes in the offspring are SS SS Ss or Ss. There is therefore a 50% chance of a child being a carrier (Ss).

2 If the parents do not have the disorder the parents must both be hh as the allele which results in the disorder is dominant (H). There is no chance of any of their children having the disorder.

Page 23

1 Bacteria producing insulin. *Note: if you know a well known example try to use it, some examiners may not have heard of more unusual ones.*

2 The programme only used a certain type of the species – the most attractive ones! The gene pool of the species was therefore reduced (there was less variety of genes present in the population). When disease struck, the gene which helped the animals fight off the disease was no longer present in the population.

3 Taking part of an organism (e.g. a cutting or a cell) and growing a new member of the species from it. The cell division is mitosis.

Page 25

1 They have become trapped in the amber where there is no oxygen present. Bacteria cannot decompose them as they cannot respire due to the lack of oxygen. *Note: it must be apparent to you that a number of examination answers rely on the fact that bacteria respire and use up oxygen when they decompose dead organisms.*

2 Any three of: X-rays, UV light, radiation, some chemicals.

3 Pale moths are camouflaged against predators where tree trunks are grey. They therefore survive to breed and dark ones are eaten. The opposite applies in industrial areas.

4 Your diagram should include: environmental change, predators wipe them out, disease wipes them out, a new species evolves which competes successfully with the species.

Environment

Page 27

1 The kestrel is the predator and the mice are prey.

2 The kestrel population would rise as there would be more food to feed their young. The mouse population would, as a result, decrease.

3 Your diagram should refer to: the amount of food available, the number of predators, disease, competition with other animals for the food available.

4 Your food web should show the two producers – seeds and berries. Birds are eating the seeds and berries, mice are eating the seeds only. The mice and birds are being eaten by the kestrels.

Page 29

1 Because a pyramid of numbers does not take account of the fact that some organisms are much larger than others (e.g. a tree and a caterpillar).

2 There are many ways including: excretion, movement, radiated as heat, all of the food is not digested in the first place.

3 There are thousands of examples. You would normally start with a producer much larger than the next stage organism (e.g. rose bush, greenfly and then ladybirds eating the greenfly).

Page 31

1 Photosynthesising, respiring, decomposing, respiring.

2 Carbohydrates, fats and proteins.

3 The dead bodies are decomposed by bacteria, the protein is broken down into ammonium compounds, the ammonium compounds are converted to nitrates by nitrifying bacteria.

Page 33

1 Sulphur dioxide given off, dissolves in rain, this makes the rain acidic as it falls on the lake. The lake water becomes acidic. Enzymes in organisms are very pH dependant. If the enzymes denature because of the acidity the organism dies. *Note: this last point on enzymes is frequently forgotten but is the most important point.*

2 The plants grow quickly, the surface of the pond will quickly become covered by plants. Many plants die. They may fall to the bottom where bacteria will decompose them. Bacteria use up oxygen in this decomposition as they are respiring. There is too little oxygen left for other animals. The process is called eutrophication.

3 You should mention: fewer trees to take it up, alongside this more is being produced by combustion (e.g. cars, power stations, burning trees).

4 The carbon dioxide in the atmosphere absorbs some radiation from the Sun which enters the atmosphere. As less is radiated back out into space the atmosphere warms up.

Classifying materials

Page 43

1 When ice melts the bonds between the water molecules have become weaker. The molecules are able to move over one another.

2 2, 8, 7.

3 Four.

4 Magnesium 2, 8, 2; silicon 2, 8, 4; argon 2, 8, 8; oxygen 2, 6.

Page 45

1 Your diagram of calcium should have 2 electrons in the first and fourth shells with eight electrons in the second and third shells.

2 Calcium needs to lose two electrons, chlorine can gain only one electron. Therefore calcium needs two chlorine atoms to react with. The formula of calcium chloride must be $CaCl_2$.

3 You should draw the structure 2, 8, 8 within a bracket. Outside of the bracket should be two positive charges.

4

2 pairs of shared electrons

Page 47

1 The bonds between molecules are generally weak and easily broken.

2 Each carbon atom is covalently bonded to four other carbon atoms. The structure is a giant structure which is rigid owing to the strong bonds between the atoms.

Oil and its uses

Page 49

1 Porous rock is likely to contain water. Oil floats on water. It cannot rise any further as non-porous rock will not let liquids through it.

2 Oil is a mixture.

3 Short-chain hydrocarbons burn easily, evaporate quite quickly and are generally gases or liquids – no use for roads! Long-chain hydrocarbons are thick (very viscous) and do not burn easily – no use for fuels!

Page 51

1 One of the bonds in the carbon–carbon double bond can break leaving the two carbon atoms free to react with another element.

2 Not all long-chain hydrocarbons can be used. There may be too much of them. They can be broken ('cracked') into short-chain hydrocarbons which may be useful as fuels, etc. Essentially they are 'cracked' so that oil companies can make more money! Alkenes also result, which can be used to make plastics.

3 They may give off chemicals which are harmful to the environment.

Page 53

1 It is increasing as more and more fuels are burned (e.g. there are more cars in the world). Therefore more gases are given off (e.g. sulphur dioxide and nitrogen oxides) which cause acid rain.

2 Partly due to the reaction between ammonia and oxygen and partly due to organisms evolving which subsequently died and decomposed releasing nitrogen. Denitrifying bacteria are involved in this nitrogen release.

3 Less carbon dioxide as it became locked up in sedimentary rocks and fossil fuels as well as being used by plants in photosynthesis. Less ammonia and methane because they reacted with oxygen (given off by plants). More oxygen due to photosynthesising plants. The oxygen also helped develop an ozone layer protecting us from the Sun's radiation (UV rays). *Note: these changes in the atmosphere questions are nearly always poorly answered, even by the best of candidates.*

Metals

Page 55

1 Copper will be displaced by the zinc as zinc is more reactive. Zinc chloride will result.

2 Your diagram should include four of: solid at room temperature, high melting points, shiny, form alloys, mostly strong and tough, good conductors of heat and electricity.

3 It is liquid at room temperature.

4 Burns with a 'squeaky' pop.

Page 57

1 To react with impurities and form molten slag.

2 It is less reactive than aluminium so nothing would happen.

3 It is melted so that electricity will be conducted. It is dissolved in molten cryolite to reduce its melting point and save the manufacturer money. *Note: if there is an economic point to make in the answer to a question then it is always advisable to mention it.*

Earth materials

Page 59

1 Their shapes seem to fit together and they seem to have similar rocks and fossils.

2 Tectonic plates sliding past each other. It is only movements of the plates that causes earthquakes. If there are no mountains then the plates cannot be moving towards each other. If they were moving apart there would be no earthquake.

3 The iron stripes are basically iron rich magma. The iron lines up in the direction of the Earth's magnetic field. This field changes. There is therefore an indication of when the magma erupted showing that the sea floor is spreading.

Page 61

1 The sedimentary rock could be forced deep below the Earth's crust. It would melt and become magma.

2 It is intrusive igneous rock usually cooling beneath the Earth's surface. The crystals are likely to be large as the rock is likely to cool quite slowly below the Earth's surface.

3 Metamorphic rocks are formed from other rocks which are put under great pressure and heat at the same time. This is most likely to occur where mountains are forming.

Page 63

1 If the igneous rock is worn away (eroded) it may eventually become sedimentary rock. If the sedimentary rock is placed under great heat and pressure then it may become metamorphic rock.

2 Sedimentary rock is continually being worn away exposing more fossils. Movements of the sedimentary rocks (e.g. folding) may result in more fossils being exposed.

3 These are formed by processes far beneath the Earth's surface. Organisms did not live there.

The periodic table

Page 65

1 The one outer electron in potassium is at a higher energy level than that of the outer electron in sodium, as it is further from the nucleus. The electron is therefore more easily 'lost'.

2 When they react with water an alkaline solution is left (e.g. sodium reacts with water to produce sodium hydroxide with hydrogen gas evolving).

3 They have a complete outer shell of electrons.

4 Xenon is present simply as single atoms. In chlorine two atoms bond together, covalently, to form a molecule of the gas (hence <u>di</u>atomic).

Page 67

1 Your diagram should include: chlorine used for killing bacteria, it is also used in disinfectants, bleaches and to produce plastics (e.g. PVC or polyvinyl chloride); hydrogen is used in the production of ammonia and margarine; sodium hydroxide is used in the production of soap, paper and ceramics.

2 Chloride ions are attracted, they lose electrons to become atoms, pairs covalently bond together to form chlorine gas molecules which evolve. *Note: in an examination a question like this could be worth 4 marks – it would be insufficient to state simply that chlorine gas evolves.*

3 They only need to gain one electron as they are only one electron 'short' in the outer shell.

4 Chlorine would displace bromine from hydrogen bromide. *Remember that reactivity decreases as you go down the group – the opposite to the alkali metals in group 1.*

Chemical reactions

Page 69

1 A reaction where one reactant is reduced whilst another reactant is oxidised.

2 A reaction where hydrogen ions are reacted with hydroxide ions.

3 potassium chloride   potassium sulphate
   calcium chloride   calcium sulphate

4 potassium hydroxide + hydrochloric acid → potassium chloride + water

or $KOH + HCl \rightarrow KCl + H_2O$

5 $SO_2 + H_2O \rightarrow H_2SO_3$ (sulphurous acid)

Page 71

1 Any three of: increase temperature – particles bump into each other more often with more energy; increase concentration – particles bump into each other more often; increase pressure (gases only) – particles bump into each other more often; increase surface area of reactants – particles bump into each other more often; use a catalyst – lowers the amount of 'activation' energy required.

2 Chemicals which speed up reactions – they are used to lower costs.

3 Make more product or make more profit.

Page 73

1 A reaction which releases heat.

2 One atom of nitrogen reacts with two atoms of oxygen, you must 'add' energy to make them react, the product is nitrogen dioxide and it is at a higher energy level than the reactants. Therefore the reaction is endothermic.

3 Endothermic (the nett energy transfer is positive).

Page 75

1 Your diagram should include: bacteria used to make yoghurt, yeast used to make alcohol and cause bread to rise.

2 A reaction which, depending on the conditions, will go either way.

3 It would be expensive to create temperatures of 350°C and equally expensive to create reaction vessels capable of withstanding pressures of 400 atmospheres.

Page 77

1 $2 \times H = 2 \times 1 = 2$
$1 \times S = 32$
$4 \times O = 4 \times 16 = 64$ Answer = 98

2 $1 \times Ca = 40$
$1 \times C = 12$
$3 \times 16 = 48$ Total = 100
of which oxygen =
or 48%

Page 78

1 $2H_2O_2$ and $2H_2O$. *Note: you will almost certainly have to balance at least one equation in the examination.*

2 M_r ammonia is 17. M_r ammonium hydroxide is 35. Therefore 34 g of ammonia will produce 2×35 g of ammonium hydroxide, or 70 g.

3 A_r magnesium is 24. Therefore 24 g of magnesium will evolve 24 litres of hydrogen. However there are 48 g of magnesium reacting. The volume of hydrogen evolved would be 2×24 litres or 48 litres.

Electricity and energy

Page 87

1 You can show how power can be calculated using this series of equations:

$$\frac{power}{(watts)} = \frac{energy\ transferred\ (joules)}{time\ (seconds)}$$

energy transferred = potential difference × charge
(joules)   (volts)   (coulombs)

charge (coulombs) = current (amps) × time

$$\frac{power}{(watts)} = \frac{potential\ difference \times current \times \cancel{time}}{\cancel{time}}$$

power = potential difference × current
(watts)   (volts)   (amps)

2 The electricity passes through a filament which offers resistance. As well as the filament becoming hot some energy is emitted as light.

Page 89

1 In the first graph: the current is directly proportional to the voltage (this means it increases at the same rate). If you reverse the voltage you reverse the current.
In the second graph: at first the current increases rapidly as you increase the voltage, however as you further increase the voltage the current increases more and more slowly. If you reverse the voltage you reverse the current.
In the third graph: the current is directly proportional to the voltage. However if you reverse the voltage you get very little current flowing at all. This component offers great resistance to current flowing in the 'wrong' direction.

2 Static electricity builds up in the clouds. If the charge becomes large enough it will jump the gap to an earthed conductor – the umbrella!

Page 91

1 $\frac{1500}{60(s)} = 25\,W$

2 $500 \times 2300 = 1\,150\,000\,J$ or $1150\,kJ$

Page 93

1 Radiation.

2 The air above the radiator warms up. It becomes less dense. The air rises. It spreads across the ceiling and cools a little. It becomes denser and so falls in other parts of the room. It is still quite warm and therefore the person feels the warmer air. Some heat will also be radiated from the radiator.

3 Air between the bricks is still likely to warm slightly – the insulation prevents convection of this air. Such convection would draw cooler air into the bottom of the wall.

Page 95

1　Hair drier as movement (the fan) and heat; toaster as heat; television as sound and light; vacuum cleaner as movement.

2　It would still save money over a long period of time. It also cuts down any noise pollution.

Page 97

1　The current is continually changing direction.

2　They can be reset quickly and work more quickly than a fuse.

3　Increase the current, or the number of turns in the coil, or place a soft iron core in the coil.

Page 99

1　There should be reference to: when you switch the current on the coil becomes an electromagnet; it reacts with the force fields of the magnets present and moves; when it becomes vertical momentum takes it past the position; the split ring keeps reversing the current so that the coil keeps spinning.

2　There should be reference to: when you switch the current on the coil becomes an electromagnet; it interacts with the magnetic field of the magnets; the coil moves in and out as a result of these interactions.

3　The current required to start a car is very high. Such a high current would require very thick, expensive wires. You would want these to be as short as possible. Therefore long, thin wires are attached to the ignition on the dashboard and when a current flows they trigger a much larger current in the short, thick wires.

Page 101

1　Examples might include:

Energy source	Advantage	Disadvantage
coal	fairly cheap	will eventually run out
hydroelectric	renewable	only useful in certain areas
nuclear	much energy from a small amount of fuel	non-renewable
wind turbine	renewable	spoils the landscape
tidal	renewable	expensive to set up

2　Hydroelectric, wind turbine, tidal.

3　Hilltops as they are exposed to the wind, coastal areas as there is more likelihood of wind, off-shore as this is less unsightly.

Page 103

1　The secondary coil has 50 times as many turns as the primary coil. The voltage induced will, therefore, be 50 times greater than the input voltage. $50 \times 200 = 10\,000$ V.

2　You want the output voltage to be $\frac{1}{25}$ of the input voltage $\frac{5000}{200}$. The ratio of primary coils to secondary coils is therefore 25:1.

Forces

Page 105

1　Average velocity = distance/time = $\frac{60}{4}$ = 15 m/s

　Acceleration = change in velocity/time = $\frac{(60 - 0)}{4} = \frac{60}{4}$ = 15 m/s^2

2　Your graph should have these features:

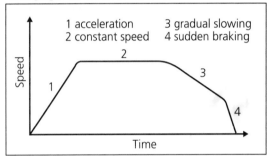

3　Velocity is speed in a straight line (velocity is a vector).

Page 107

1　For example, if your mass is 57 kg then your weight is 57×10 N or 570 N.

2　The downward force due to the weight of the boat (due to gravity) is balanced by the upward force of the water.

3　There is a backward force exerted by the car engine. There is a force resisting this caused by both air resistance and the friction of the tyres on the ground. The forces are unbalanced so the car moves backwards.

4　Kinetic energy = $\frac{1}{2}$mv^2
　Therefore ($\frac{1}{2} \times 100) \times 30^2$.
　This equals 50×900 or 45 000 J or 45 kJ.

Page 109

1　Force = mass × acceleration.
　Therefore force = $1000 \times 6 = 6000$ N. *Note: the weight of the car was 10 000 N therefore its mass is 1000 kg.*

2　Work done = force × distance. The force is therefore 10 000 N × 50 m or 500 000 J or 500 kJ.

3　The force of gravity causes the stone to accelerate as it falls. At a certain speed the pressure of the air prevents the stone falling any faster. The forces are now balanced and the stone falls at steady speed. This steady speed is known as the terminal velocity. *Note: never answer this question just by stating 'terminal velocity'. The question asks what has happened not what is it called.*

Page 111

1 The master cylinder: pressure = force/area so the pressure is $\frac{20}{0.1}$ or 200 N/m². The slave cylinder: force = pressure × area so the force = 200 × 0.4 or 80 N.
Note: the calculation can be done using simple ratios. The slave cylinder has an area 4 times that of the slave cylinder. The force it exerts will be 4 times greater: 4 × 20 = 80 N.

2 The pressure is so great and there is no light.

Waves and radiation

Page 113

1 As the light passes from one substance into a substance of a different density it changes speed. This change of speed results in the light bending. This is known as refraction.

2
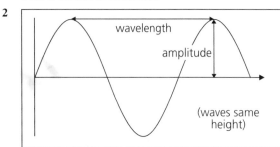

Page 115

1 They are checking for structural defects (e.g. cracks).

2 P waves travel through solids and liquids. S waves only pass through liquids. They both refract as they pass into substances of a different density. *(Note: liquids will also change in density.)* If you know the point of the Earth the shock wave starts from and where it can be detected as it is felt at a different point of the Earth's surface, then you can work out the densities of the substances it has passed through to result in the refraction the wave has experienced.

Page 117

1 X-rays (shortest), UV, microwave, radio waves (longest).

2 Any two of: electric grills, toasters, heaters, optical fibres and video remote controls.

3 The white light from the Sun passes through water droplets. The light is refracted to different extents and therefore the colours are seen.

Page 119

1 A light is shone down the endoscope. The light totally internally reflects so emerges only at the end of the endoscope. It internally reflects because the angle at which the light 'hits' the side of the endoscope is greater than the critical angle.

2 As the water enters the harbour entrance the waves spread out from the edges and cause the boat to 'bob'. This is known as diffraction.

Page 121

1 UV radiation. Advantages might include giving people a sun tan and making them feel better within themselves. Disadvantages might include burns and possible skin cancer.

2 Beta and gamma radiation will pass through very thick paper.

3 Uranium loses an alpha particle (two protons and two electrons). Thorium loses a beta particle (and one proton becomes a neutron).

Page 123

1 200 years (two half-lives).

2 Uranium has 92 protons and 92 electrons (so as an atom is electrically neutral). It has 146 neutrons.

3 They use control rods to absorb the neutrons (these are generally made of boron or cadmium).

The Universe

Page 125

1 Weather, communication, to see the Universe without atmospheric interference.

2 Placed in orbit high above the equator, at the same speed as the Earth is spinning.

3 So that the Earth spins below; the whole of the Earth can be scanned in a day.

4 In the stable period the star stays the same size as the forces of attraction (between all of the particles, due to gravity) and repulsion (due to the very high temperatures) are balanced. The forces of repulsion will start to 'win' and the star will become a red giant. These forces then begin to decrease and so the force of gravity becomes the larger force. The star contracts to become a white dwarf. If the star was large enough and contraction takes place quickly then it may explode and become a supernova. A very dense neutron star remains.
Note: a question about this may be worth about 5 marks – do not waffle make sure that you write down five correct facts in the right order.

Page 126

1 As galaxies are moving apart quickly the wavelength of light is increasing. As it increases red light moves into the far red part of the spectrum. This is known as the 'red shift'.

2 As galaxies move away light is shifted to the red end of the spectrum.

Index